MATRIX

H. S. GREEN

MECHANICS

with a foreword by
MAX BORN

P. NOORDHOFF LTD - GRONINGEN - 1965 - THE NETHERLANDS

Contents

Preface

This book contains material which has been presented in lectures to third year students at the University of Adelaide for a number of years.

These students have had a separate course on matrix algebra, and my experience has been that by following these courses even the less gifted students acquire a good basic understanding of quantum mechanics and the ability to solve a range of interesting problems.

This little book may also be of interest to those who already have a knowledge of quantum mechanics and wish to see the subject from a point of view different from that adopted in most elementary text-books.

H. S. GREEN

Foreword

Lecturing or writing a textbook means selecting the essential features from an enormous and ever increasing material. One has to perform a sort of balance act between historical and logical truth. Research tends to make round-about ways; following them up would never lead to the up-to-date situation.

Though my knowledge of modern textbooks on quantum mechanics is rather scanty, I have the impression that there is a tendency to neglect the historical roots and to build the theory on foundations which have actually been discovered later. This method undoubtedly arrives quickly at modern problems and is well suited for producing experts able to apply what they have learned. But I doubt whether it is a good training for doing original research, because it fails to show how the pioneer finds his way in the jungle of unordered facts and obscure theoretical attempts. The present book is not a compromise between teaching science as it was discovered and as it is today, but a kind of clever combination of the two aspects. It might be called "idealized history".

It begins with a realistic historical introduction which seems to me (who was one of the actors in the play), for all its brevity, essentially correct.

Then follows a systematic development which is an improved version of the method used by the Göttingen school (matrix mechanics). It is mathematically rigorous and general enough to include also the approach of de Broglie and Schrödinger (wave mechanics). This is achieved with the help of ordinary operator and matrix terminology and notation; the ingenious formalism invented by Dirac for the same purpose is not used in the text but explained in an appendix.

The physical foundations are handled with similar simplicity; they correspond roughly to Heisenberg's original ideas, later of course generalised to include Dirac's relativistic theory.

There is a short section on quantum-mechanical paradoxes, which are discussed with the help of a sharp distinction between the indeterminate *(unbestimmt)* and uncertain *(ungewiss)*. I think the solutions thus obtained are perfectly convincing.

Though I am naturally a little prejudiced in favour of the Göttingen version which is emphasised here - others may have different tastes - I can say with confidence that this little book offers a new and easy way of learning quantum mechanics to anybody who can think mathematically. The methods often differ from the usual ones; they are original and need concentrated study. But those who spend some effort and time on them will acquire a thorough understanding of the theory. I recommend it warmly to teachers and students.

MAX BORN

Bad Pyrmont, October 1964

Historical Introduction

The quantum theory had its origin at the beginning of the twentieth century when Planck [1] * was investigating the thermodynamical equilibrium of matter and radiation, with the object of explaining the observed distribution of energy with frequency in *black-body* radiation. He was faced with the problem of interpolating between the theory of Rayleigh, which agreed well with the observed spectrum at low frequencies, and the theory of Wien, which was good at high frequencies. By reasoning which could best be described as plausible, he arrived at a relation between the energy density and frequency which was in excellent agreement with the experiments over the whole spectrum. The theoretical interpretation of his result required that radiation of angular frequency ω should be absorbed and emitted by matter only in integral multiples of the basic 'quantum' $\hbar\omega$, where $\hbar = 1.054 \times 10^{-27}$ erg sec is known as Planck's constant.

Planck was inclined to attribute this *atomic* nature of radiation, which he had discovered, to the properties of the matter by which it was emitted. It was left to Einstein [2] to deduce that the relation $E = \hbar\omega$ between the energy E and the angular frequency of a quantum must be an intrinsic property of the radiation, independent of its source. Having arrived at this conclusion, Einstein saw that it should be possible to obtain experimental confirmation by means of the photo-electric effect. His reasoning was based on the consideration that a fixed amount of energy E' should be required to extract an electron from a metal. If radiation of a given frequency ω fall on the metal, and consist of quanta of energy $E = \hbar\omega$, electrons will be ejected if, and only if $E > E'$. This is, in fact, what is found experimentally in the photo-electric effect.

---

* Numbers in [ ] refer to the list of references at the end of this book.

1

The proof of the atomicity of radiation by Planck and Einstein was only the first step in the development of the quantum theory. Before any further step could be made it was necessary to achieve a better understanding of the structure and mechanics of the atom. Rutherford's experiments showed that an atom consisted of a positively charged nucleus, surrounded by enough electrons to secure electrical neutrality. They also provided evidence that the forces between electrons and nuclei, even at short distances, are primarily of an electrostatic nature. This picture of an atom consisting of charged particles and held together by electrostatic forces, however, was hard to reconcile with classical electrodynamics, which had been perfected by Maxwell and Lorentz before the present century. According to this theory, a system of charged particles should be inherently unstable. Under the influence of their mutual attractions, the negative charges should accelerate towards the positive charges and lose energy continuously by radiation. The electrons in Rutherford's atom should spiral into the nucleus, with release of unlimited energy in the form of radiation. Of course this is not what happens.

The clue to the mystery of the unwonted stability of atoms came from the investigation of their spectra by the spectroscopists. It was found that the radiation emitted by excited atoms was not distributed through the whole spectrum, as classical electrodynamics would lead one to expect, but confined to a set of characteristic frequencies. In hydrogen, these frequencies were given empirically by Balmer's formula:

$$\omega^{(m,\,n)} = R(m^{-2}-n^{-2}),$$

where m and n are integers, and satisfied Ritz's combination principle:

$$\omega^{(m,\,n)} = \omega^{(m)}-\omega^{(n)}, \quad \omega^{(m)} = R/m^2.$$

This result was interpreted by Bohr as an affirmation of the conservation of energy in the emission of radiation by an atom. He noticed that if one multiplied the frequency relation by Planck's constant, one obtained

$$\hbar\omega^{(m,\,n)} = E^{(m)}-E^{(n)} \quad (E^{(m)} = \hbar\omega^{(m)}),$$

where $\hbar\omega^{(m,\,n)}$ was the energy of the quantum of radiation emitted by the atom, and $E^{(m)}$ and $E^{(n)}$ could be regarded as the energies of the atom in the initial (excited) and final states, respectively. Looked at in this way, the spectrocopic data implied that the energy of the internal state of the atom was not arbitrary, but had to take one of the fixed values $E^{(m)}$, $m = 1, 2, 3, \ldots$ This was, of course, completely consistent with the observed stability of atomic structure, though it did not account for the failure of classical electrodynamics.

The next idea of fundamental significance in the progress of quantum mechanics came from de Broglie [3], in 1923. He suggested an interpretation of the relation $E^{(m)} = \hbar\omega^{(m)}$ between the energy $E^{(m)}$ and the term $\omega^{(m)}$ which appeared in the combination principle. Just as the photon, the quantum of radiation, had associated with it a frequency $\omega = E/\hbar$, and other attributes of a wave, the electron in an atom (de Broglie reasoned) had associated with it the frequency $\omega^{(m)} = E^{(m)}/\hbar$ and other attributes of a wave. If one took account of the fact that a stationary wave surrounding the nucleus could have only an integral number of wave-lengths, this might account for the connection between the frequencies $\omega^{(m)}$ and the positive integers m. This initially rather vague idea was given a precise mathematical form in 1926, by Erwin Schrödinger [4]. In the course of a few elegant papers, he developed the whole apparatus of wave mechanics, which we recognize today as a complete and valid system for the explanation and prediction of atomic phenomena.

We have mentioned each of four men, Planck, Einstein, de Broglie and Schrödinger, above, as playing a vital part in the development of quantum mechanics. Their contributions are justly emphasized in nearly all the elementary text-books on the subject. Yet it is a remarkable and ironic fact that not one of them ever reached an understanding of quantum mechanics which allowed him to give assent to the accepted theory. Planck expressed his ultimate views in his book. 'The Universe in the Light of Modern Physics'. He stated [5]: *Now, if the Quantum Theory were superior or equal to the classical theory at all points, it would be not only feasible but necessary to abandon the latter*

3

in favour of the former. This, however, is definitely not the case .. It is not the case that the Quantum Theory cannot be applied, but that, when applied, the results reached do not agree with experience. Einstein [6] wrote, not long before his death in 1955: *For, if the statistical quantum theory does not pretend to describe the individual system (and its development in time) completely, it appears unavoidable to look elsewhere for a complete description of the individual system . . . the elements of such a description are not contained within the conceptual scheme of the statistical quantum theory. With this one would admit that, in principle, this scheme could not serve as a basis of theoretical physics.* Earlier, Einstein had crystallized certain of his objections to the quantum theory by specifying experimental situations in which, he thought, the quantum theory predicted paradoxical results; in all such situations, however, the actual experiments merely served to confirm the theory.

De Broglie has confessed his astonishment at the form which the quantum theory, that he had helped to found, finally assumed. In the years 1925—1927, he endeavoured to build a rival theory, but abandoned the attempt when the success of the established theory became evident. However, he more recently revived this effort, and his conclusion [7] remains that *the quantum theory will perhaps appear to us one day as having provided only a statistical representation of certain aspects of an underlying physical reality which it was unable to describe completely.* Schrödinger [8] was more caustic in defining his final attitude: *The new science (q.m.) arrogates the right to bully our whole philosophical outlook. It is pretended that refined measurements which lend themselves to easy discussion by the quantum-mechanical formalism could actually be made. They could not . . . Actual measurements on single individual systems are never discussed in this fundamental way, because the theory is not fit for it.*

It would be easy to gain the impression, from these dissenting statements from men of unsurpassed eminence, that quantum mechanics is, or was, the subject of intense controversy. However, that would be quite wrong. There are in contemporary physics still some adherents to the views expressed by Einstein and de

4

Broglie, notably Janossy [9] and Bohm and Vigier [10]; however, it cannot be said that they have made any substantial impression on the development of scientific thought. A more interesting question is why those who did so much to assist in the development of quantum mechanics should recoil from the consequences of their handiwork. We shall return to this question when we have completed our survey of the historical development of the subject.

In the year 1925, when de Broglie's wave model of the electron had gained currency, but Schrödinger's work in Zürich on the foundations of wave mechanics was not yet complete, Heisenberg [11] sketched out a new and very original approach to the mechanics of the atom, in Born's school at Göttingen. It was not yet a correct version of quantum mechanics, but contained several very suggestive ideas, which were taken up by Born and Jordan [12] during a short absence of Heisenberg from Göttingen. Together they formulated the matrix mechanics of a particle in one dimension; after Heisenberg had returned, and joined them, the generalization for three dimensions was obtained and published in a celebrated paper by Heisenberg, Born and Jordan [13].

So, by 1926, there were two apparently very different ways of solving the problems of atomic physics: Schrödinger's wave mechanics, and the matrix mechanics of Heisenberg, Born and Jordan. It was, however, soon realized that the two methods, though apparently disconnected, were in one sense equivalent and in another sense complementary. Schrödinger [14] was the first to show why the two methods should lead to identical results, in their common domain of application. Born [15] made the wave-mechanical approach his own, by applying it to as yet unsolved problems involving the scattering of one particle by another. Bohr [16] played an important part in working out the physical and philosophical implications of the theory, to which Einstein and Schrödinger particularly took such strong objection. The next step was the synthesis of the two methods by Dirac [17]. After this there was a rapid expansion of the fields of applications. A relativistic quantum mechanics of particles of spin half was found by Dirac, and the quantum mechanics of fields was developed for the pure radiation field by Dirac [17], and for general electrodynamics by Heisenberg and Pauli [18]. The most important developments since 1945 have been the development of quantized relativistic field theories and the application of new techniques to nuclear physics.

We are now in a better position to speculate on why Planck, Einstein, de Broglie and Schrödinger were so much discomforted by the revolution in the description of atomic phenomena which took place in 1925. They had this in common, that they were accustomed to the imaginative representation of events in space and time. Einstein especially had cause to remember the successes of the general theory of relativity, in which the future as well as the past is represented with the present as a space-time continuum, and matter is simply one aspect of the geometry of the continuum. It was impossible to reconcile this picture with the indeterminacy which was an essential part of the new quantum mechanics. Schrödinger also had a deep feeling for general relativity, and in addition a conviction, shared by de Broglie, that the waves described by his wave equations had an objective physical significance. Quantum mechanics denies that the waves of wave mechanics have anything more than a statistical significance, and, even so, only in relation to a particular type of experiment. This might be a difficult thing to accept by anyone who regarded wave mechanics as a brilliant discovery, not to mention the brilliant discoverer himself.

The above brief historical sketch is intended to atone in part for any lack of respect for the historical development of quantum mechanics in the account which follows, and also to draw attention to the motive for writing (or reading) this account. Most books on the quantum theory emphasize the wave mechanical approach, probably because it is supposed to be easier for anyone who already has a good knowledge of differential equations. But unless the reader is aware that wave mechanics is only a special rendering of quantum mechanics, in the co-ordinate representation, he will be apt to acquire the same ideas of the importance of the co-ordinate representation and the physical significance of the wave function which evidently misled some of our greatest physicists. There is a great gain of physical understanding to be obtained from reading the subject as it was first presented in Born and Jordan's book [19]. The present account is intended to provide a contemporary exposition of the matrix method, with the simplifications made possible by the avoidance of special representations.

The technique of matrix mechanics is much improved by use of the *factorization method*, which was first discovered by Schrödinger [20], in the context of wave mechanics, and developed by Infeld and Hull [21]. This is used consistently for the solution of eigenvalue problems in the following. The project material at the end of each chapter is partly a recapitulation and extension of the text, but contains also a few problems taken from the author's own work [22].

1. The Mathematical Basis of Quantum Mechanics

The object of quantum mechanics is to predict the results of physical measurements in which atomic systems (particles, atoms or molecules) are concerned. Some types of experiments determine the behaviour of large numbers of similar systems, and the measurements therefore reflect the behaviour of the individual systems only in a statistical way. Other types of experiments, in which cloud chambers, bubble chambers, photographic emulsions and counters play a part, determine the behaviour of individual systems directly, and a large number of measurements on similar systems have to be made to obtain statistically significant. results The predictions of quantum mechanics are therefore concerned with specifying the possible results of a measurement, and the probability that any one of these results will be obtained. Sometimes the possible results are well separated from one another; this is so, for instance, if they relate to the angular momentum of a system of particles or the energy levels of a bound state like an atom or an atomic nucleus. Otherwise the results are distributed over a range of values; this is so, for instance, if they relate to the time of decay of a radioactive nucleus or the angle of deflection of a particle which collides with another.

Since quantum mechanics is concerned with the results of measurements, and measurements may be regarded as operations on physical systems, it is not surprising that the mathematics required to describe these procedures at a fundamental level should be the mathematics of *operators*. Operators appear in mathematics in various forms; the simplest operators are those represented by matrices. A matrix equation of the type

$$A\psi = \phi, \text{ i.e., } \sum_{l=1}^{n} A_{kl}\psi_l = \phi_k$$

$(k = 1, 2, \ldots n)$ says in effect that, by a certain operation, the vector ψ with components ψ_1, ψ_2, ... ψ_n is transformed into the vector ϕ with components ϕ_1, ϕ_2, ... ϕ_n. The operator which effects this transformation is completely specified by the matrix $[A_{kl}]$. In matrix mechanics, one is often concerned with vectors and matrices with an infinite number of components and elements, respectively. In most instances, including those which will arise in what follows, the infinity is *countable*, so that the components of a vector are in correspondence with the positive integers. But there are instances where the infinity is uncountable, and the equation $A\psi = \phi$ has to be interpreted as an integral equation, e.g., $\int A(k, l)\psi(l)\mathrm{d}l = \phi(k)$. In wave mechanics, one is mainly concerned with operators which are differential operators, so that $A\psi = \phi$ is interpreted as a linear differential equation. In developing the formal auxiliary mathematics, we shall try to keep in mind all these possibilities.

1.1 *Vectors in Hilbert Space*

The symbols ϕ, ψ, χ, ... will be used to represent *vectors*, whose essential properties are listed as (a), (b), (c) below. In quantum mechanics, we shall be concerned with vectors in *Hilbert space*, which have the property (d) also.

(a) Any two vectors ϕ, ψ are either identical $[\phi = \psi]$ or not identical $[\phi \neq \psi]$. If $\phi = \psi$, then $\psi = \phi$; and if $\phi = \psi$ and $\psi = \chi$, then $\phi = \chi$.

(b) Any two vectors ϕ, ψ have a sum $\phi+\psi$, which is itself a vector. Vector addition is commutative $[\phi+\psi = \psi+\phi]$ and associative $[\phi+(\psi+\chi)=(\phi+\psi)+\chi]$. By definition, $\phi+\psi+\chi = \phi+(\psi+\chi)$.

(c) If a is any number (real or complex), any vector ϕ has a product $a\phi$ which is itself a vector. Multiplication by a number is distributive

$$[a(\phi+\psi) = a\phi+a\psi \text{ and } (a+b)\phi = a\phi+b\phi], \quad 1\psi = \psi \text{ and } 0\psi = \mathbf{0},$$

where $\mathbf{0}$ represents the *null vector**. By definition, $\phi-\psi = \phi+(-1)\psi$.

(d) Any pair of vectors ϕ, ψ have a *scalar product*, denoted

---

* Whenever there is no likelihood of confusion, the null vector will be represented by 0.

by (ϕ, ψ) or $\phi^*\psi$, which is a real or complex number, and has the following properties:

(i) $(\phi, \phi) \geq 0$ and $(\phi, \phi) = 0$ if and only if $\phi = \mathbf{0}$;

(ii) $(\phi, \psi+\chi)=(\phi, \psi)+(\phi,\chi)$ and $(\phi, a\psi) = a(\phi, \psi)$;

(iii) $(\phi, \psi)=(\psi, \phi)^*$,

where $(\psi, \phi)^*$ means the *complex conjugate* of (ψ, ϕ). It should be noticed that $(a\phi, \psi)=(\psi, a\phi)^* = [a(\psi, \phi)]^* = a^*(\phi, \psi)$.

We mention two examples of vectors in Hilbert space.

(1) A finite or infinite sequence of real or complex numbers $\phi_1, \phi_2, \phi_3, \ldots$ is a vector, provided

(a) the identity of two sequences $\phi_1, \phi_2, \phi_3, \ldots$ and $\psi_1, \psi_2, \psi_3, \ldots$ implies $\phi_k = \psi_k$ for $k = 1, 2, 3, \ldots$;

(b) the sum of two sequences $\phi_1, \phi_2, \phi_3, \ldots$ and $\psi_1, \psi_2, \psi_3, \ldots$ is defined as the sequence $\phi_1+\psi_1, \phi_2+\psi_2, \phi_3+\psi_3, \ldots$;

(c) the product of a number a and the sequence $\phi_1, \phi_2, \phi_3, \ldots$ is defined as the sequence $a\phi_1, a\phi_2, a\phi_3, \ldots$, so that the sequence $0, 0, 0, \ldots$ is the null vector;

(d) the scalar product of the sequences $\phi_1, \phi_2, \phi_3, \ldots$ and $\psi_1, \psi_2, \psi_3, \ldots$ is defined by $(\phi, \psi) = \phi_1^*\psi_1+\phi_2^*\psi_2+\phi_3^*\psi_3+ \ldots$, or $\phi^*\psi = \Sigma_k\phi_k^*\psi_k$. Vectors of this kind are commonly used in matrix mechanics; they may be called vectors in *sequence space*. The numbers $\phi_1, \phi_2, \phi_3, \ldots$ are called *components* of the vector ϕ.

(2) A function $\phi(x)$ of a real variable x, defined and continuous in any range $b < x < c$, is a vector, provided

(a) the identity of $\phi(x)$ and $\psi(x)$ implies $\phi(x) = \psi(x)$ for $b < x < c$;

(b) the sum of $\phi(x)$ and $\psi(x)$ — in the sense of vector theory — is defined as

$$\phi(x)+\psi(x);$$

(c) the product of a and $\phi(x)$ — in the sense of vector theory — is defined as

$$a\phi(x);$$

(d) the scalar product of $\phi(x)$ and $\psi(x)$ is defined by

$$(\phi, \psi) = \int_b^c \phi^*(x)\psi(x)\mathrm{d}x.$$

Vectors of this kind are usual in wave mechanics, and may be called vectors in *function space*.

A finite or countably infinite set of vectors $\psi^{(1)}$, $\psi^{(2)}$, ... is said to be *complete*, if any vector of the same space can be expressed in the form $\psi = \sum_j c_j \psi^{(j)}$, where the c_j are numbers. The vectors of the set $\psi^{(1)}$, $\psi^{(2)}$, ... are said to be *independent*, if any relation of the type $\sum_j c_j \psi^{(j)} = \mathbf{0}$ between them implies that all the c_j are zero. The null vector obviously cannot be one of an independent set of vectors.

The number $||\phi|| = (\phi, \phi)^{\frac{1}{2}}$, i.e., the square root of the scalar product of the vector ϕ with itself, is called the *norm* or the *length* of the vector ϕ. If $||\phi|| = 1$, ϕ is said to be *normal*. Any vector ϕ, except the null vector $\mathbf{0}$, can be *normalized* by dividing by $||\phi||$. If $\phi^* \psi = 0$, i.e., if $(\phi, \psi) = 0$, the vectors ϕ and ψ are said to be *orthogonal*.

Suppose we have a set of independent vectors $\psi^{(j)}$, where $j = 1, 2, \ldots$, and that there is no other vector independent of these, so that the set is complete. We can then always construct from them a set of normal vectors $\delta^{(j)}$, which are orthogonal to one another, i.e., such that $(\delta^{(k)}, \delta^{(j)}) = 0$ when $j \neq k$. The construction proceeds as follows: $\delta^{(1)}$ is obtained by normalizing $\psi^{(1)}$:

$$\delta^{(1)} = \psi^{(1)} / ||\psi^{(1)}||.$$

Then $\delta^{(2)}$ is obtained by subtracting from $\psi^{(2)}$ the *component* $(\delta^{(1)}, \psi^{(2)})\delta^{(1)}$ of $\psi^{(2)}$ along $\delta^{(1)}$, and normalizing the result

$$\delta^{(2)} = [\psi^{(2)} - (\delta^{(1)}, \psi^{(2)})\delta^{(1)}] / ||\psi^{(2)} - (\delta^{(1)}, \psi^{(2)})\delta^{(1)}||.$$

Since $(\delta^{(1)}, \delta^{(1)}) = 1$, $(\delta^{(1)}, \delta^{(2)}) \propto (\delta^{(1)}, \psi^{(2)}) - (\delta^{(1)}, \psi^{(2)}) = 0$. Let $\delta^{(j)}$ be defined recursively by

$$\delta^{(j)} = [\psi^{(j)} - \sum_{k=1}^{j-1} (\delta^{(k)}, \psi^{(j)})\delta^{(k)}] / ||\psi^{(j)} - \sum_{k=1}^{j-1} (\delta^{(k)}, \psi^{(j)})\delta^{(k)}||.$$

If we assume that $(\delta^{(l)}, \delta^{(k)}) = 0$ when k and l differ and both are less than j, it follows that $(\delta^{(l)}, \delta^{(j)}) \propto (\delta^{(l)}, \psi^{(j)}) - (\delta^{(l)}, \psi^{(j)}) = 0$; thus $(\delta^{(l)}, \delta^{(k)}) = 0$ when $k = j$ also. So we verify by induction that $(\delta^{(k)}, \delta^{(j)}) = 0$ whenever $j \neq k$. Note that

11

$\psi^{(j)} - \sum_{k=1}^{j-1} (\delta^{(k)}, \psi^{(j)})\delta^{(k)}$ cannot vanish, as otherwise there would be a relation between $\psi^{(1)}$, $\psi^{(2)}$, ... and $\psi^{(j)}$. The vectors $\delta^{(j)}$ form what is known as an *ortho-normal set*.

A set of vectors $\delta^{(1)}$, $\delta^{(2)}$, ... defined by the method just described is complete, because the set $\psi^{(1)}$, $\psi^{(2)}$, ... was complete; hence an arbitrary vector ψ can be represented in the form

$$\psi = \sum_j \psi_j \delta^{(j)}.$$

The vector ψ can, therefore, be represented as a vector in sequence space, with components ψ_1, ψ_2, ... defined by the above relation. It is easy to verify that

(a) $\phi = \psi$ implies $\phi_j = \psi_j$, for $j = 1, 2, \ldots$, and the converse;

(b) $(\phi + \psi)_k = \phi_k + \psi_k$;

(c) $(a\phi)_k = a\phi_k$;

(d) $(\phi, \psi) = \sum_k \phi_k^* \psi_k$.

The notation which has been used above for the representation of vectors is quite common and will be used consistently in the following. The reader should, however, also be familiar with an auxiliary notation, due to Dirac, which is explained in the Appendix.

1.2 *Linear operators*

A *linear operator* A is a correspondence, or rule, by which a vector $A\psi$ is associated with any vector ψ, in such a way that

(i) if $\phi = \psi$, then $A\phi = A\psi$;

(ii) $A(c\psi) = c(A\psi)$;

(iii) $A(\phi + \psi) = A\phi + A\psi$.

If A and B are linear operators, and ψ is any vector,

(a) cA denotes the operator defined by $(cA)\psi = c(A\psi)$;

(b) $A + B$ denotes the operator defined by $(A + B)\psi = A\psi + B\psi$;

(c) AB denotes the operator defined by $(AB)\psi = A(B\psi)$;

(d) $\mathbf{1}$ denotes the operator defined by $\mathbf{1}\psi = \psi$.

1.3. *Representation of linear operators by matrices*

Suppose the number of independent vectors in a space is not

more than countably infinite, and $\delta^{(1)}$, $\delta^{(2)}$, ... is an ortho-normal set constructed as described in 1.1. Any vector ψ can be expressed in the form $\sum_k \psi_k \delta^{(k)}$; in particular, $\delta^{(j)}$ can be expressed as $\sum_k \delta_k^{(j)} \delta^{(k)}$, where

$$\delta_k^{(j)} = \delta_{jk} = \begin{cases} 1, & j = k, \\ 0, & j \neq k. \end{cases}$$

If A is any linear operator and A_{kl} are the components of the vector $A\delta^{(l)}$, the components of $A\psi$ are

$$(A\psi)_k = \sum_l (\psi_l A\delta^{(l)})_k = \sum_l A_{kl}\psi_l.$$

The complete set of components $[A_{kl}]$ is a *matrix* which is said to represent the linear operator A. The linear operator **1** is represented by the diagonal matrix $[\delta_{kl}]$.

If the ortho-normal set $\delta^{(j)}$ $(j = 1, 2, \ldots)$ is infinite, the matrix $[A_{kl}]$ is an infinite matrix, which may be displayed in the form

$$A = \begin{bmatrix} A_{11} & A_{12} & A_{13}\cdots \\ A_{21} & A_{22} & A_{23}\cdots \\ A_{31} & A_{32} & A_{33}\cdots \\ \cdots\cdots\cdots\cdots\cdots \\ \cdots\cdots\cdots\cdots\cdots \end{bmatrix},$$

but, as the number of rows and columns is infinite, it is not, of course, possible to show all the elements. If, however, the vectors are in a space of n dimensions, there is only a finite number n of the $\delta^{(j)}$, and the matrix has n^2 elements which can be displayed in n rows and n columns.

1.4 *Application to complex numbers*

A complex number is usually defined as an ordered set of two real numbers, i.e., in the present terminology, as a vector $\{\psi_k\}$ with two real components ψ_R and ψ_I. This vector is usually denoted by $\psi_R + \mathbf{i}\psi_I$.

A linear operator $\mathbf{i}$ can be defined by

$$(\mathbf{i}\psi)_R = -\psi_I, \qquad (\mathbf{i}\psi)_I = \psi_R;$$

13

it is represented by the matrix

$$\begin{bmatrix} 0 & -1 \\ 1 & 0 \end{bmatrix}.$$

If a, b, a', b' are real numbers,

$$(a1+bi)(\psi_R+i\psi_I) = (a\psi_R-b\psi_I)+i(a\psi_I+b\psi_R),$$
$$(a1+bi)(a'1+b'i) = (aa'-bb')1+(ab'+ba')i.$$

Other linear operators are:

C (complex conjugate of), defined so that

$$C\psi = \psi^* = \psi_R+i(-\psi_I),$$

i.e., so that

$$(C\psi)_R = \psi_R \text{ and } (C\psi)_I = -\psi_I.$$

R (real part of), defined so that

$$R\psi = \psi_R,$$

i.e., so that

$$(R\psi)_R = \psi_R \text{ and } (R\psi)_I = 0.$$

I (imaginary part of), defined so that

$$I\psi = i\psi_I,$$

i.e., so that

$$(I\psi)_R = 0 \text{ and } (I\psi)_I = \psi_I.$$

Ex. 1: Prove that

(i) $R+I = 1$, $R-I = C$,

(ii) $iC+Ci = 0$, $C^2 = 1$, $(Ci)^2 = 1$,

(iii) $R^2 = R$, $I^2 = I$, $RI = IR = 0$,

and find the matrix representations of C, R, I and Ci.

1.5 Eigenvectors and eigenvalues

If $A\psi = a\psi$, where a is a number, a is called an *eigenvalue* of A, and ψ the corresponding *eigenvector* (assumed not to vanish).

If A and B have a common eigenvector ψ, then $(AB-BA)\psi=0$. For, if a and b are the eigenvalues, $(AB)\psi = A(B\psi) = A(b\psi)$

14

$= ab\psi$, and, similarly, $(BA)\psi = ba\psi$. It follows that, if every eigenvector of A is also an eigenvector of B, then $AB = BA$, i.e., A and B *commute*.

The following discussion of eigenvalues and eigenvectors applies *only* when the number of dimensions n of the vector space S is *finite*. Methods for finding eigenvalues and eigenvectors when S is infinite but countable will be given later. To determine the eigenvalues and eigenvectors when n is finite, let $D(a)$ be the determinant

$$D(a) \equiv |a\delta_{kl} - A_{kl}|.$$

Elimination of the components ψ_l from the simultaneous equations

$$\sum_{l=1}^{n} A_{kl}\psi_l = a\psi_k \tag{1}$$

yields the equation $D(a) = 0$. As $D(a)$ is a polynomial of the n-th degree in a, it can be expressed in the form

$$D(a) = \prod_{j=1}^{n} (a - a^{(j)}),$$

and the numbers $a^{(j)}$ are then the eigenvalues of A. When these have been determined, solution of the first $n-1$ equations (1), for each $a^{(j)}$, allows $\psi_2{}^{(j)}, \psi_3{}^{(j)}, \ldots \psi_n{}^{(j)}$ to be found in terms of $\psi_1{}^{(j)}$, which is arbitrary. Another way of finding the eigenvectors, when the function $D(a)$ has been calculated, will appear below.

We first show that the eigenvectors of an operator A form a complete set of independent vectors, if no two of the eigenvalues $a^{(j)}$ are equal. If $\psi^{(j)}$ $(j = 1, 2, \ldots n)$ are the eigenvectors, it must be shown that a relation of the type $\sum_{j=1}^{n} c_j\psi^{(j)} = \mathbf{0}$ implies $c_j = 0$ for all j. Applying the operator A to this relation, one finds $\sum_{j=1}^{n} c_j a^{(j)}\psi^{(j)} = \mathbf{0}$, and likewise $\sum_{j=1}^{n} c_j(a^{(j)})^m\psi^{(j)} = \mathbf{0}$ for $m = 0, 1, 2, \ldots n-1$. The Vandermonde determinant $|(a^{(j)})^{k-1}|$ does not vanish [it is equal to $\prod_{j=2}^{n} \prod_{k=1}^{j-1} (a^{(j)} - a^{(k)})$] when the eigenvalues are all distinct; therefore $c_j\psi^{(j)} = \mathbf{0}$ for each value of j. As $\psi^{(j)} \neq \mathbf{0}$, $c_j = 0$, which was to be proved.

15

If two of the eigenvalues of A are equal, the above proof fails, and, in fact, the eigenvectors form a complete set then only if the operator A satisfies special conditions (e.g., if it is hermitean).

Next we show that the operator A satisfies the same equation $D(A) = 0$ as its eigenvalues. Assuming that the eigenvalues $a^{(j)}$ of A are all distinct, the eigenvectors, as just proved, form a complete set, and an arbitrary vector can be expressed in the form

$$\psi = \sum_{j=1}^{n} c_j \psi^{(j)}.$$

Applying the linear operator $D(A)$ to this equation, we have

$$D(A)\psi = \sum_{j=1}^{n} c_j D(a^{(j)}) \, \psi^{(j)} = 0,$$

and, as ψ is arbitrary, $D(A) = 0$. This result can also be proved if some of the eigenvalues of A coincide. For, if δA is an operator with arbitrary small matrix elements δA_{kl}, the eigenvalues $a^{(j)} + \delta a^{(j)}$ of $A + \delta A$ will be distinct, and satisfy a determinantal equation of the form $D(a + \delta a) + \delta D(a + \delta a) = 0$. The argument already given shows that $D(A + \delta A) + \delta D(A + \delta A) = 0$, and when $\delta A = 0$, this leaves us with $D(A) = 0$.

Ex. 2: Verify directly that the matrix $[A_{kl}]$ satisfies the equation $D(A) = 0$, when $n = 2$.

We can now show that if ψ is any vector, and $\psi^{(1)} = \{\prod_{j=2}^{n} (A - a^{(j)})\}\psi$ does not vanish, the latter is an eigenvector of A corresponding to the eigenvalue $a^{(1)}$. For

$$(A - a^{(1)})\psi^{(1)} = D(A)\psi = 0.$$

One can always find a vector ψ such that $\psi^{(1)}$ does not vanish, if necessary by trying each of the complete set of vectors $\delta^{(j)}$, with components δ_{jk} defined in 1.3. Thus the eigenvectors of A can be constructed from the formula

$$\psi^{(j)} = \{\prod_{k(\neq j)} (A - a^{(k)})\}\psi.$$

Finally, if the eigenvectors of A form a complete set, the

16

coefficients in the expansion $\psi = \sum_j c_j \psi^{(j)}$ can be determined by multiplying by $\prod_{k(\neq j)} (A - a^{(k)})$; this gives

$$1 = c_j \prod_{k(\neq j)} (a^{(j)} - a^{(k)}).$$

If

$$P^{(j)} = c_j \prod_{k(\neq j)} (A - a^{(k)}),$$

the expansion can be written

$$\psi = \sum_j P^{(j)}\psi.$$

Ex. 3: (a) Verify directly that $\sum_j P^{(j)} = 1$, by using the identity

$$\frac{1}{D(a)} \equiv \sum_{j=1}^n \frac{c_j}{(a - a^{(j)})}.$$

(b) Show that $(P^{(j)})^2 = P^{(j)}$ and $P^{(j)}P^{(k)} = 0$ when $j \neq k$.

1.6 Special types of operators

(a) Projective operators

An operator P satisfying $P^2 = P$ is called a *projective* (sometimes, an *idempotent*) operator. Its eigenvalues are obviously all zeros and ones.

Examples: the operators R and I introduced in 1.4; the operator $P^{(j)}$ introduced in 1.5.

(b) Hermitean operators

If $(A\phi)^*\psi = \phi^*(A^*\psi)$ for arbitrary vectors ϕ and ψ, the linear operator A^* is called the *hermitean conjugate* of A. If the index set S is countable, a necessary and sufficient condition for this condition to be satisfied is obviously

$$(A\delta^{(k)})^*\delta^{(l)} = \delta^{(k)}(A^*\delta^{(l)}), \text{ i.e., } (A_{lk})^* = (A^*)_{kl}.$$

If $A^* = A$, i.e., if $(A_{lk})^* = A_{kl}$, the operator A is called *hermitean*.

The eigenvalues of a hermitean operator are all real. For, if A is hermitean, and $A\psi = a\psi$ where $\psi \neq 0$, the equation $(A\psi)^*\psi = \psi^*(A\psi)$ yields $a^*\psi^*\psi = a\psi^*\psi$; and, as $\psi^*\psi$ is necessarily positive, $a^* = a$.

17

Eigenvectors corresponding to distinct eigenvalues of a hermitean operator are orthogonal. For $(A\psi^{(j)})^*\psi^{(k)} = (\psi^{(j)})^*A\psi^{(k)}$ yields $a^{(j)}(\psi^{(j)})^*\psi^{(k)} = a^{(k)}(\psi^{(j)})^*\psi^{(k)}$, so that if $a^{(j)} \neq a^{(k)}$, $\psi^{(j)*}\psi^{(k)} = 0$. Even if $a^{(j)} = a^{(k)}$, it is possible to find orthogonal eigenvectors corresponding to the equal eigenvalues. This is done, for example, by introducing an operator δA with arbitrary small matrix elements δA_{kl}. The eigenvalues $a^{(j)}+\delta a^{(j)}$ of $A+\delta A$ are distinct, and their eigenvectors are orthogonal, by the argument already given. Thus, if $j \neq k$, $(\psi^{(j)}+\delta\psi^{(j)})^*(\psi^{(k)}+\delta\psi^{(k)}) = 0$, and this reduces to $\psi^{(j)*}\psi^{(k)} = 0$ when $\delta A \to 0$.

Orthogonal vectors are necessarily independent; hence the set of eigenvectors of a hermitean matrix is complete.

(c) Unitary operators

A *unitary* operator U has the property that, if U^* is its hermitean conjugate, $U^*U = \mathbf{1}$.

The eigenvalues of a unitary operator are all of *modulus* 1. For, if $U\psi = \lambda\psi$, the relation $(U\psi)^*(U\psi) = \psi^*(U^*U\psi) = \psi^*\psi$ reduces to $\lambda^*\lambda\psi^*\psi = \psi^*\psi$.

Ex. 4: Determine the eigenvalues and normalized eigenvectors of the operator represented by $[A_{kl}]$, where k and l take the values 1 and 2 only. Determine the projective operators $P^{(1)}$ and $P^{(2)}$ defined as in 1.5, and prove that

$$A = a^{(1)}P^{(1)}+a^{(2)}P^{(2)},$$
$$A^2 = (a^{(1)})^2P^{(1)}+(a^{(2)})^2P^{(2)}.$$

Ex. 5: If A is hermitean, and $\psi = \sum_j c_j\psi^{(j)}$, $\phi = \sum_j d_j\psi^{(j)}$, where the $\psi^{(j)}$ are the orthogonal normalized eigenvectors of A, show that $\phi^*\psi = \sum_j d_j^*c_j$. Show also that if $(\psi^*\psi)(\phi^*\phi)\cos^2\theta = (\psi^*\phi)(\phi^*\psi)$, then $-1 \leq \cos\theta \leq 1$.

1.7 *Functions of operators*

The square and higher powers of an operator A, and polynomials in A are already defined by means of 1.2 (a)—(d). It is also possible to define a function $f(A)$ of an operator A, provided

18

(i) $f(a)$ exists when a is any eigenvalue of A; and

(ii) the set of eigenvectors of A is complete.

For let ψ be an arbitrary vector, and let $\psi = \sum_j c_j \psi^{(j)}$ be the development of ψ in terms of the eigenvectors of A, assumed here to be countable. Then $f(A)$ can be defined by means of

$$f(A)\psi = \sum_j c_j f(a^{(j)}) \psi^{(j)}.$$

If $P^{(j)}$ is the projective operator for the eigenvector $\psi^{(j)}$, i.e.,

$$P^{(j)}\psi = c_j \psi^{(j)},$$

then

$$f(A) = \sum_j f(a^{(j)}) P^{(j)}.$$

Important functions which can be defined in this way are: A^{-1}, the reciprocal of A, which exists if A has no vanishing eigenvalue (and its eigenvectors form a complete set), and the function $\exp(\alpha A)$.

Ex. 6: Prove that if A is hermitean, $\exp(iA)$ exists and is unitary. Prove also that if A and B commute, $\exp(A+B) = \exp A \cdot \exp B$.

1.8 Canonical Transformations

A canonical transformation is one under which every vector ψ is replaced by a vector $\psi' = U\psi$, and every linear operator A by a linear operator $A' = UAU^*$, where U is a unitary operator. Since $U^* = U^{-1}$, every equation of this section is unchanged by the transformation. For example, $A\psi = \phi$ implies $UAU^*U\psi = U\phi$, i.e., $A'\psi' = \phi'$; and $B = A_1 A_2$ implies $UBU^* = UA_1 U^* UA_2 U^*$, i.e., $B' = A'_1 A'_2$, while $\phi^*\psi = c$ yields $(U\phi)^*U\psi = c$, i.e., $(\phi')^*\psi' = c$. A canonical transformation may be pictured as a rotation of the *axes of reference* in Hilbert space.

If $\{\psi^{(j)}\}$ is any complete set of normal and mutually orthogonal vectors, one can find a canonical transformation such that $\psi^{(j)'} = \delta^{(j)}$, i.e., $\psi_k^{(j)'} = \delta_{jk}$. For, on account of the *ortho-normal* property, $\psi^{(k)*}\psi^{(j)} = \sum_l \psi_l^{(k)*} \psi_l^{(j)} = \delta_{jk}$. Setting $U_{kl} = \psi_l^{(k)*}$, this relation can be written $U\psi^{(j)} = \delta^{(j)}$. Also, if U^* is the hermitean conjugate of the operator U, so that $U^*_{kl} = (U_{lk})^* = $

$= \psi_k{}^{(l)}$, the relation $\psi^{(k)}{}^* \psi^{(j)} = \delta_{jk}$ reads $UU^* = 1$; thus, U is a unitary operator.

If the $\psi^{(j)}$ are the normalized eigenvectors of an operator A, the relation $A\psi^{(j)} = a^{(j)}\psi^{(j)}$ transforms to $A'\delta^{(j)} = a^{(j)}\delta^{(j)}$, i.e., $A'_{kj} = a^{(j)}\delta_{kj}$. So, after the canonical transformation, A is represented by a diagonal matrix whose diagonal elements are the eigenvalues of A (and A').

1.9 *Synopsis of Classical Mechanics*

The classical mechanics of a system of particles is conveniently summarized in the Lagrangian formalism. Suppose that the instantaneous configuration of the entire system is specified by means of a number of coordinates q_1, q_2, q_3, q_4, ... (possibly, but not necessarily, cartesian). In classical mechanics, the q_r are of course not linear operators but numbers. The *Langrangian function L* of the system is an explicit function of the q_r, their time derivatives $\dot{q}_r$, and perhaps also the time:

$$L = L(q_1, q_2, \ldots; \dot{q}_1, \dot{q}_2, \ldots; t).$$

The *momentum p_r* which is canonically conjugate to the coordinate q_r is obtained by differentiating L with respect to the corresponding *velocity $\dot{q}_r$*:

$$p_r = \partial L / \partial \dot{q}_r.$$

The *force F_r*, equal to the rate of change of the momentum p_r, is obtained by differentiating L with respect to q_r:

$$\frac{\mathrm{d}p_r}{\mathrm{d}t} = F_r = \frac{\partial L}{\partial q_r}.$$

The *equations of motion* of the system of particles are obtained by substituting $r = 1, 2, 3, \ldots$ in the above. The *energy* of the system is

$$H = -L + \sum_r p_r \dot{q}_r.$$

Since

20

$$\frac{\mathrm{d}L}{\mathrm{d}t} = \frac{\partial L}{\partial t} + \sum_r \left(\frac{\partial L}{\partial q_r} \dot{q}_r + \frac{\partial L}{\partial \dot{q}_r} \frac{\mathrm{d}\dot{q}_r}{\mathrm{d}t} \right)$$

$$= \frac{\partial L}{\partial t} + \sum_r \left(\frac{\mathrm{d}p_r}{\mathrm{d}t} \dot{q}_r + p_r \frac{\mathrm{d}\dot{q}_r}{\mathrm{d}t} \right)$$

$$= \frac{\partial L}{\partial t} + \frac{\mathrm{d}}{\mathrm{d}t}(H+L),$$

we see that $\mathrm{d}H/\mathrm{d}t = 0$ if $\partial L/\partial t = 0$, i.e., the energy is conserved provided L does not depend explicitly on the time.

In Newtonian mechanics, L is expressed as the difference between the *potential energy* V of the system, which is usually a function $V(q_1, q_2, \ldots)$ of the coordinates only, and the *kinetic energy* T:

$$L = T - V(q_1, q_2, \ldots).$$

If cartesian coordinates are adopted,

$$T = \sum_r (\tfrac{1}{2} m_r \dot{q}_r{}^2),$$

where m_r is the mass associated with the r-th co-ordinate; the equations of motion are

$$m_r \frac{\mathrm{d}\dot{q}_r}{\mathrm{d}t} = -\frac{\partial V}{\partial q_r},$$

and the energy is

$$H = \sum_r (\tfrac{1}{2} m_r \dot{q}_r{}^2) + V.$$

If and only if V depends only on differences of coordinates, and not on the absolute position of any particle, we shall have

$$\sum_r \frac{\partial V}{\partial q_r} = 0,$$

from which it follows that the total momentum of the system of particles is conserved:

$$\frac{\mathrm{d}}{\mathrm{d}t} \left(\sum_r p_r \right) = 0.$$

Alternatively, the Hamiltonian formalism may be used to summarize the results of classical mechanics. If the energy H

is expressed as a function of the q_r and p_r (and, possibly, the time),

$$H = H(q_1, q_2, \ldots, p_1, p_2, \ldots; t),$$

the function $H(q_1, q_2, \ldots; p_1, p_2, \ldots; t)$ is called the *Hamiltonian function* of the system of particles. The velocity $\dot{q}_r$ can be obtained by differentiating the Hamiltonian with respect to p_r

$$\dot{q}_r = \frac{\partial H}{\partial p_r},$$

and the equations of motion of the system can be written in the form

$$\dot{p}_r = -\frac{\partial H}{\partial q_r}.$$

In Newtonian mechanics, $p_r = m_r \dot{q}_r$ and H has the form $H = \sum_r (\frac{1}{2}p_r^2/m_r) + V$.

EXAMPLES I

1. Write down the fundamental properties of a set of vectors. Consider the functions which have the following properties:
  (i) each function $\phi(x)$ has a derivative $\phi'(x)$ for $a < x < b$, and
  (ii) $\phi'(x+\varepsilon) + \phi'(x-\varepsilon) - 2\phi'(x)$ tends to zero as ε tends to zero, for $a < x < b$. Prove that these functions constitute a set of vectors, i.e., have all the required properties, provided (a) the vector sum of $\phi(x)$ and $\psi(x)$ is defined as the ordinary sum $\phi(x) + \psi(x)$; (b) the null vector is the special 'function' 0, and the negative of the vector $\phi(x)$ is defined as $-\phi(x)$; (c) the product of the number a and the vector $\phi(x)$ is defined as $a\phi(x)$ [Note that it is necessary, among other things, to show that $\phi(x) + \psi(x)$, $-\phi(x)$ and $a\phi(x)$ are vectors when $\phi(x)$ and $\psi(x)$ are vectors, to furnish an adequate proof]. Is $\phi'(x)$ necessarily a vector, when $\phi(x)$ is a vector?
2. Prove *from first principles* that, if ϕ, ψ, $\chi \ldots$ are vectors,
  (i) $$0\phi = \mathbf{0},$$
  (ii) $$a\mathbf{0} = \mathbf{0},$$
  (iii) $$a\phi + b\psi = \tfrac{1}{2}(a+b)(\phi+\psi) + \tfrac{1}{2}(a-b)(\phi-\psi).$$

3. Write down the definition of a linear operator. If A, B, C are linear operators, how are $A+B$, AB, $A+B+C$, and $A-B$ defined? Prove *from first principles* that $(A+B)^2=A^2+AB+BA+B^2$. If $[A, B]$ means $AB-BA$, prove that

$$[A, B^3]=[A, B]B^2+B[A, B]B+B^2[A, B],$$

and find a similar expression for $[A, B^4]$. Also, prove that $[A, [B, C]]+[B, [C, A]]+[C, [A, B]] = 0$. If $\{A, B\}$ means $AB+BA$, show that

$$\{A, BC\}=[A, B]C+B\{A, C\}$$

and

$$[A, BC]=\{A, B\}C-B\{C, A\}=[A, B]C-B[C, A].$$

4. Let A and B be linear operators with the properties $A^2 = B^2 = 1$ and $\{A, B\} = AB+BA = 0$. Let $C = -iAB$. Prove that $C^2 = 1$, and $\{A, C\}=\{B, C\} = 0$. Show that the eigenvalues of A are -1 and $+1$. If ϕ is an eigenvector of A corresponding to the eigenvalue $+1$, show that $B\phi$ is an eigenvector of A corresponding to the eigenvalue -1, and that $(C-iB)\phi = 0$. Prove that $(aA+bB+cC)^2=(a^2+b^2+c^2)1$; hence, or otherwise, find the eigenvalues of $aA+bB+cC+d1$.

5. Show that the *norm* (length) of a vector ϕ is a real number $||\phi||$ with the following properties:

(i) $||\phi|| \geqq 0$ and $||\phi|| = 0$ if and only if $\phi = 0$;

(ii) $||\phi+\psi|| \leqq ||\phi||+||\psi||$;

(iii) $||a\phi||=|a| \, ||\psi||$, where $|a|$ is the modulus of the possibly complex number a. Show that

$$(\phi, \psi) = \tfrac{1}{4}[||\phi+\psi||^2-||\phi-\psi||^2+i||\phi-i\psi||^2-i||\phi+i\psi||^2],$$

if (ϕ, ψ) is the scalar product of ϕ and ψ.

6. Let A and B be linear operators with the properties $A^3 = A$, $B^3 = B$, and $A^2B+BA^2 = B$. Show that $ABA = 0$, $A^2B^2=B^2A^2$, and that if $AB-BA = iC$, then $C^3 = C$, $CA-AC = iB$ and $A^2C+CA^2 = C$. Prove that the eigenvalues of A are -1, 0 and 1. If $B^2A+AB^2 = A$ is added to the properties already assumed, then $BAB = 0$ and $BC-CB = iA$.

23

7. What is the fundamental property of a *hermitean* linear operator? Prove that $(AB)* = B*A*$. Show that if B is hermitean and $A*B = BA$, then it follows from $A\psi = a\psi$ that either a is real or $(\psi, B\psi) = 0$.

8. What is meant by a *unitary* linear operator? Prove that the reciprocal of a unitary operator is unitary, and that the product of two unitary operators is unitary. If $A^2 = B^2 = 1$, $AB+BA=0$ and $C = -iAB$, find the reciprocal of the operator $aA+bB+cC+d1$, assuming $a^2+b^2+c^2 \neq d^2$. Prove that the operator $\cos\theta\,1+i\sin\theta\,A$ is unitary, if A is hermitean.

9. If $(A-\alpha_1 1)(A-\alpha_2 1) = 0$, and ϕ is any vector which is *not* an eigenvector of A, then $A\phi-\alpha_2\phi$ and $A\phi-\alpha_1\phi$ are eigenvectors of A. Generalize this result to find the eigenvectors of B, where $(B-\beta_1 1)(B-\beta_2 1)(B-\beta_3 1) = 0$.

10. Define the *determinant* of a matrix, and calculate the determinant

$$|A| = \begin{vmatrix} a & b & c & d \\ -d & a & b & c \\ -c & -d & a & b \\ -b & -c & -d & a \end{vmatrix}$$

directly. Now show that the matrix can be expressed in the form

$$A = a1+bQ+cQ^2+dQ^3,$$

where Q is a certain matrix. Prove that $Q^4 = -1$; find the eigenvalues of Q and those of A. Hence verify, for the particular matrix A, that the determinant of a matrix is the product of its eigenvalues. Determine the eigenvectors of Q and A.

2. The Physical Basis of Quantum Mechanics

In classical physics two of the most useful models for the purpose of understanding physical phenomena are the particle, visualized as a moving point, and the wave, depicted as analogous to a wave on water or on a vibrating string. Though these models are also useful in quantum mechanics, neither is fully adequate for the description of the elementary particles, and it is very necessary to appreciate their uses and limitations. The reader is reminded that in the nineteenth century the theory of Maxwell tended to establish the view that light, and various other forms of radiation, consisted of electromagnetic waves. This view was, however, very hard to reconcile with the discovery, by Planck and Einstein, that electromagnetic radiation of angular frequency ω and wave-length $2\pi\lambda$ consists of indivisible 'photons' of energy $E = \hbar\omega$ and momentum $p = \hbar/\lambda$. Still more surprising was de Broglie's hypothesis, confirmed by appropriate diffraction experiments, that electrons, previously regarded as classical particles, had some of the characteristics of a wave, including an angular frequency ω and a wave-length $2\pi\lambda$ which were related to their relativistic energy E and momentum p by the same formulae. Obviously, some new concept was needed to harmonize the apparent contradiction in supposing that photons, electrons and other particles could combine the attributes of a moving point and a wave.

It is permissible to mistrust anything but the evidence of the senses, and to resolve such a contradiction we might well start with an examination of the apparatus by means of which individual particles are detected and studied. The following devices are commonly used:

(1) The cloud chamber: When a charged particle traverses a chamber filled with saturated vapour, it ionizes certain of the atoms in the neighbourhood of its path. To operate the chamber,

the vapour is decompressed, so that the now supersaturated vapour condenses in droplets on the ions, and reveals the approximate path of the particle. If the chamber is placed in a magnetic field **B**, the track of a particle of mass m and charge e has the radius of curvature $cp/(eB)$, measurement of which determines the momentum p.

(2) The photographic emulsion. The passage of a charged particle displaces electrons in nearby grains of the emulsion, and this in turn leads to the displacement of other electrons, so that the affected grains become visible on development and again the approximate path of the particle is revealed.

(3) The bubble chamber. Today this has widely displaced the cloud chamber, from which it differs in containing a liquid at the boiling point instead of vapour at the point of condensation. The liquid is superheated by decompression, and bubbles form on ions produced by the passage of a charged particle.

(4) The counter. In various forms this detects an energetic particle by the initiation of a cascade of electrons whose impulse can be amplified and recorded. A single counter records the approximate position and time of arrival of a particle; two or more counters in coincidence or delayed coincidence may record the track and mean velocity of the particle. Particles which are uncharged are detected by means of their reactions with charged particles when emitted or absorbed.

The common feature of the devices described above is that they are so designed that even the minute interaction of a single particle is sufficient to produce an effect of macroscopic dimensions, normally through the transition of some component from a metastable to a thermodynamically stable state.

Let us now keep in mind the means by which the presence of individual particles is perceived, and consider an experimental situation in which the conflict between the two concepts of a particle, as a moving point and as a wave, is most acute. This was, with other similar situations, the subject of argument between Bohr and Einstein in the years 1928 to 1930. Electrons or photons are emitted from source S and are absorbed at a photographic plate P after diffraction through a pair of slits A and B in a screen, as shown in Fig. 1. It is found that the

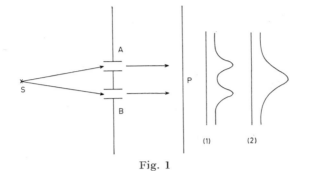

Fig. 1

diffraction pattern (1) produced at P by the absorption of a large number of particles is quite different from the pattern (2) which results from blocking the slit A, and then the slit B for the same time. By suitably reducing the intensity of the source S, it can be verified that the patterns are produced by the impact of a succession of particles, each of which is absorbed at a definite point on the plate P, and that the patterns do not change, so that there is no possibility that a particle passing through one slit could influence a second particle passing through the other slit.

Now, if the particles were moving points which had to pass through either A or B (and not both), the pattern produced by equal numbers of particles passing through each of the two slits should not be affected by whether the other slit was closed at the time. We may therefore exclude the possibility that the particles have a definite position (either A or B) in passing through the screen, when both slits are open. On the other hand, each particle arrives at a definite point on the plate P. We can only conclude that a particle does not have a definite position, except where experimental arrangements are made to determine its position! Moreover, since the particle has no definite position at the screen, there is no possibility to predict which slit a given particle will pass through. Of course, if the photographic plate is moved to a position just behind the screen, it will be verified

27

experimentally that a given particle passes through one slit and not the other. But this will change the experimental arrangement and prevent the observation of the diffraction pattern which we originally described. Moreover, the possibility of predicting which slit the particle will pass through is of course not changed by the movement of P behind the screen.

Any physical variable, like the position vector of the particle at the screen, which has no definite value unless experimental arrangements are made to measure it, is said to be *indeterminate*. It is necessary to distinguish carefully between indeterminacy and uncertainty, the equivalents in English of the German words *Unbestimmtheit* and *Ungewissheit*. A physical quantity which is merely *uncertain* has a definite value, which, however, is unknown to the experimenter. The indeterminacy is removed from any measurable characteristic of a particle or system of particle, at the time when the particle or system interacts with an efficient measuring device, which produces a corresponding effect at the macroscopic level. As the author has shown [23], it is simply the huge number of particles in the macroscopic system which guarantees that the indeterminacy is reduced to an insignificant level. Until the experimenter takes note of the change which has occurred in his apparatus, the value of the measured quantity remains uncertain; thereafter, its value is certain.

2.1 *The Quantum-Mechanical Paradoxes*

It is instructive to consider, in the light of what has already been said, certain paradoxes which have been propounded by various eminent dissentients to the established principles of the quantum theory.

(1) Schrödinger's Cat Paradox

Schrödinger was responsible for the following 'thought experiment'. A sound-proof, opaque box is equipped with a shutter designed to open just long enough to admit a photon. Inside the box, opposite the shutter, is a half-silvered mirror, made to reflect just 50 % of all photons falling on it, and transmit the rest. If a photon is reflected, nothing will happen. However, if a photon is transmitted, it will operate a counter, also in the box, which is electrically connected to a loaded gun. A cat is imprisoned in the box, and if the photon operates the counter, the gun will fire and the cat will lose the last of its seven lives. Now suppose the shutter is made to open. According to Schrödinger, it is indeterminate whether the photon is reflected or transmitted by the half-silvered mirror; therefore it is indeterminate whether the counter operates and the gun fires; therefore it is indeterminate whether the cat is alive or dead. Only when the box is opened and the experimenter looks inside, does the indeterminacy disappear and the cat flickers from a state of suspended judgement into life or death. Nobody would believe this conclusion, and so the whole concept of indeterminacy is in question.

The reader should easibly find the flaw in the above argument. In fact, the indeterminacy disappears when the photon interacts, or fails to interact, with the counter, after which it can only be uncertain whether the cat lives or dies.

(2) De Broglie's Paradox

The following paradox, due to de Broglie, is more puzzling at first glance. A closed box in Paris, with reflecting interior walls, contains a single particle. Without attempting to locate the particle, a reflecting double partition is inserted, which divides the box into two equal halves. The two halves are separated and one of the resulting boxes is sent to Tokyo. It is thus quite indeterminate whether the box in Paris contains the particle. An experiment is now made in Tokyo to determine whether the other box contains the particle or not. At the moment when this question is resolved, it becomes certain whether the box in Paris contains the particle, and the indeterminacy is removed. Thus an experiment in Tokyo produces an immediate effect in Paris, without any possibility of communication between the two cities.

Surely this is beyond credibility?

There is nothing in the situation imagined by de Broglie

which is not already present in any experiment in which the position of a particle is determined; the wide separation postulated for the two boxes merely serves to underline the obvious absurdity in supposing that determinacy is propagated like light from one point to another. On the other hand, without this separation, there seems to be nothing remarkable in the fact that the detection of a particle at one point precludes its appearance at another. From the physical point of view, nothing beyond the conservation of the number of particles is involved.

In the absence of any contradiction or problem, the quantum theorist maintains that there is no real paradox to be resolved.

(3) Paradox of Einstein, Rosen and Podolsky [24]

De Broglie's paradox is very similar in one respect to a well known paradox advanced by Einstein, Rosen and Podolsky, (ERP) in an attempt to show that quantum mechanics provides only an incomplete description of physical systems. However, the paradox of ERP draws attention to another question, concerning the compatibility of measurements of the position and the velocity of the same particle. Let us first state the content of the paradox.

Consider two particles which collide and separate; their total momentum $\mathbf{p} = \mathbf{p}_1 + \mathbf{p}_2$ may be supposed to be known, but their separate momenta $\mathbf{p}_1$ and $\mathbf{p}_2$ are indeterminate. It is also permissible to suppose that their relative position vector $\mathbf{r} = \mathbf{q}_2 - \mathbf{q}_1$ is known, but their separate positions $\mathbf{q}_1$ and $\mathbf{q}_2$ are necessarily indeterminate. If, now, the momentum of one particle, say $\mathbf{p}_1$, is measured, the momentum of the other becomes determinate. If, however, the position vector $\mathbf{q}_1$ is measured, the position of the other becomes determinate. There are two odd things about this:

(1) The measurement of a quantity relating to one particle affects the determinacy of a quantity relating to a second particle, which may be far away from the place where the measurement is made.

(2) Either the position or the momentum of the second particle can be made determinate, whereas quantum mechanics claims that they cannot both be determinate.

30

The first part of the paradox (if it admits of this description) is like de Broglie's paradox, except that the total momentum and the relative position are the variables whose values are prescribed. It would clearly be very unsatisfactory if the measurement of p_1 or q_1 did not suffice to make p_2 or q_2, respectively, determinate! The second part of the paradox is resolved by taking note of the fact that the apparatus needed to measure p_1 is different from that needed to measure q_1 and these measurements are mutually exclusive — just as, in the diffraction experiment illustrated in Fig. 1, the location of the particles just behind the screen would exclude the possibility of the observation of the diffraction pattern, and conversely. The paradox of ERP was based on the misconception that a quantity which can be made determinate becomes an element of reality, even though it is not measured.

The impossibility which we have noticed in predicting the results of certain measurements which can be made on a particle or system of particles is a distinctive feature of quantum mechanics. In classical mechanics, such predictions are made on the basis of the equations of motion of the system, and a knowledge of the positions and velocities of the particles at some initial time. In quantum mechanics, there are, as we shall see, equations of motion identical in form with those of classical mechanics, but it is physically impossible to obtain a knowledge of the positions and velocities.

The analysis of a physical experiment shows that in general three things are involved:

(1) the system observed;
(2) the measuring apparatus;
(3) the observer who notes the result of the measurement.

In macroscopic physics, it can be assumed, under ideal conditions, that (1) is unaffected by (2) and (2) is unaffected by (3). Although there is necessarily some interaction between (1) and (2), and between (2) and (3), it is assumed that these interactions can be made so small that neither the behaviour of (1) nor the functioning of (2) is affected. There is a tendency also to assume

31

that the interaction between (2) and (3) is immaterial; that the result of the measurement is predictable and could be calculated by the observer if necessary.

Where the system observed is of atomic dimensions, however, these assumptions require re-examination. It is no longer true that the interaction between (1) and (2) can be made so small that the behaviour of the system is unaffected. Since the measuring apparatus is necessarily of a macroscopic nature, the interaction between (2) and (3) may be neglected; but it is not usually true that the observer can predict the result of the measurement.

Because of the interaction between the system observed and the measuring apparatus, certain measurements are incompatible; the performance of one measurement precludes the possibility of performing another. For example, suppose it is desired to measure the distance r between two electrons with a probable error less than Δr. This can be done by allowing the interaction of the system of electrons with radiation of wave-length of the order of Δr. But such radiation causes the electrons to recoil, with the result that their relative velocity undergoes fluctuations proportional to $(\Delta r)^{-1}$. The accurate measurement of the relative velocity of the electrons is therefore precluded by the measurement of their relative distance. Quite generally, the simultaneous accurate measurement of a co-ordinate q and the corresponding velocity $\dot{q}$ is impossible; as the accuracy of one measurement increases, the possible accuracy of the other measurement decreases. It is not possible, therefore, to provide 'initial conditions' for the prediction of the behaviour of atomic systems, in the way contemplated by classical physics. This is accepted by quantum theory not merely as an experimental difficulty, but as a fundamental law of nature.

Quantum theory nevertheless admits the possibility of predictions of two kinds:

(1) Although one cannot predict the result a of a measurement, one can usefully predict that the result will belong to a set of values $\{a^{(j)}\}$.

(2) One can also usefully predict the *probability* $p^{(j)}$ that the result of the measurement will be $a^{(j)}$. This asserts that, if a

sufficiently large number of identical experiments is made, the fraction of the total number, in which the result of the measurement is $a^{(j)}$, will be $p^{(j)}$, with arbitrarily small error.

The numbers $a^{(j)}$ are a property of the observed system; the probabilities $p^{(j)}$ are a property of the *state* of the system, depending on the way the identical experiments were prepared.

The possible results of a measurement are conveniently identified with the (real) eigenvalues $a^{(1)}$, $a^{(2)}$, . . . of a hermitean operator A, which is said to represent the quantity measured. A hermitean operator representing a measurable quantity is called an *observable*. Two different measurements may be compatible or incompatible. If they are compatible, the observables A and B representing the measured quantities will have simultaneous eigenvalues $a^{(j)}$, $b^{(k)}$, and common eigenvectors $\psi^{(jk)}$ such that $A\psi^{(jk)} = a^{(j)}\psi^{(jk)}$ and $B\psi^{(jk)} = b^{(k)}\psi^{(jk)}$. As already noticed in 1.5, the condition for this is that A and B should commute. However, if the measurements are incompatible, the observables A and B will have no simultaneous eigenvalues, and A and B do not commute. In classical physics, all measurements are assumed to be compatible, and the observables representing all measured quantities quite properly commute; the operators may then be replaced by numbers. In quantum physics, however, we are already prepared for the fact that the observables representing a co-ordinate and the corresponding velocity should not commute.

The state of an atomic system is conveniently represented by a vector ψ. If ψ is expanded in terms of the eigenvectors $\psi^{(j)}$ of an observable A, thus: $\psi = \Sigma_j c_j \psi^{(j)}$, the term $c_j \psi^{(j)}$ represents the *possibility* that the measurement of the corresponding quantity will yield the eigenvalue $a^{(j)}$. Alternatively, we can regard the vector ψ as representing an arbitrarily large number of identical systems, and the term $c_j \psi^{(j)}$ then represents those which, on measurement, yield the eigenvalue $a^{(j)}$. According to Born, to whom the statistical interpretation of quantum mechanics is due, if the vector ψ and the eigenvectors $\psi^{(j)}$ are all normalized, the number $c_j^* c_j$ is the probability that the measurement will yield the eigenvalue $a^{(j)}$. Since (see Ex. 5, p. 18)

$\Sigma_j c_j * c_j = 1$, the probabilities are not only positive, but add up to 1, as of course they should. The average measured value is

$$\Sigma_j c_j * c_j a^{(j)} = \psi * A \psi.$$

To summarize:

2.1 Physical Interpretation

(1) A hermitean linear operator (observable) represents a measurable quantity, and its eigenvalues the results of the measurement. If the simultaneous measurement of two different quantities is possible, the observables representing these quantities commute; otherwise, they fail to commute.

(2) A normalized vector represents the state of an atomic system (alternatively, an assembly of identical systems). The projection of this vector on a normalized eigenvector $\psi^{(j)}$ of an observable A represents the possibility that the measurement of the corresponding quantity will yield the eigenvalue $a^{(j)}$ (alternatively, those members of the assembly which, on measurement, yield the eigenvalue $a^{(j)}$).

(3) The probability that the eigenvalue $a^{(j)}$ of A will be measured, in a state represented by ψ, is $c_j * c_j$, where $c_j \psi^{(j)}$ is the projection of ψ along the normalized eigenvector $\psi^{(j)}$. The average measured value A is $\psi * A \psi$.

It follows, of course, that if the state of the system is prepared so that the eigenvalue $a^{(j)}$ is certain to be measured, the state vector ψ is an eigenstate of A.

2.2 Commutation Rules Involving the Energy

If two measurements are incompatible, the corresponding observables A, B do not commute, and one needs the value of their commutator $AB-BA$. We first consider the commutator $AH-HA$ of any observable A with the observable H representing the total energy of an atomic system. This was deduced by Heisenberg, with Born's assistance, in somewhat the following way.

Following the researches of Planck and Einstein, the relation

$$E = \hbar\omega$$

between the energy E of a quantum of radiation, the angular frequency ω, and Planck's constant $\hbar$ ($\hbar = 1.0544 \times 10^{-27}$ erg sec.) was well known in 1925. Thus, if an atom emitting a quantum of radiation of frequency ω has energy $E^{(i)}$ in the initial state and $E^{(f)}$ in the final state,

$$E^{(i)} - E^{(f)} = \hbar\omega. \tag{2.1}$$

If $\psi^{(i)}$ and $\psi^{(f)}$ are eigenvectors of the energy H of the atom, corresponding to the eigenvalues $E^{(i)}$ and $E^{(f)}$,

$$H\psi^{(i)} = E^{(i)}\psi^{(i)}; \quad H\psi^{(f)} = E^{(f)}\psi^{(f)}.$$

Thus it follows from (2.1) above that

$$\psi^{(f)*}(AH - HA)\psi^{(i)} = (E^{(i)} - E^{(f)})\psi^{(f)*}A\psi^{(i)}$$
$$= \hbar\omega\psi^{(f)*}A\psi^{(i)}.$$

Now it was reasonably assumed by Heisenberg that the *matrix element* $\psi^{(f)*}A\psi^{(i)}$ of any observable A connected with the atom would vary harmonically with time, with the same frequency as the radiation emitted, i.e., that

$$i\frac{d}{dt}(\psi^{(f)*}A\psi^{(i)}) = \omega\psi^{(f)*}A\psi^{(i)}.$$

Thus

$$\psi^{(f)*}(AH - HA)\psi^{(i)} = i\hbar\frac{d}{dt}(\psi^{(f)*}A\psi^{(i)}).$$

Assuming further that the vectors $\psi^{(i)}$ and $\psi^{(f)}$ do not change with time, this leads to

$$\boxed{AH - HA = i\hbar\frac{dA}{dt}}. \tag{2.2}$$

This *commutation relation* will be adopted as a postulate, suggested by experiment.

NOTE: If Heisenberg had assumed that the vectors $\psi^{(i)}$ and $\psi^{(f)}$, but not the operator A, varied with the time, he would have arrived at *Schrödinger's equation*

$$i\hbar\frac{d\psi^{(i)}}{dt} = H\psi^{(i)}.$$

This is the basis of wave mechanics, an apparently quite different theory which is, however, equivalent to matrix mechanics.

2.3 Constants of the Motion

As a first deduction from (2.2), if the operator A is a constant of the motion, so that $dA/dt = 0$, one has $AH=HA$. Thus any constant of the motion can be measured together with the energy.

2.4 Commutation Rules between Coordinates and Momenta

Consider a particle moving in a certain direction in a field of potential $V(q)$, depending on the co-ordinate q. The total energy is

$$H = \tfrac{1}{2}m\dot{q}^2 + V(q),$$

where $\dot{q} = dq/dt$. The relation

$$qH - Hq = i\hbar\dot{q}$$

reduces to

$$\tfrac{1}{2}m(q\dot{q}^2 - \dot{q}^2q) = i\hbar\dot{q},$$

which can be written

$$\tfrac{1}{2}m(q\dot{q} - \dot{q}q)\dot{q} + \tfrac{1}{2}m\dot{q}(q\dot{q} - \dot{q}q) = i\hbar\dot{q}.$$

This is obviously satisfied by taking

$$m(q\dot{q} - \dot{q}q) = i\hbar$$

or, setting $p = m\dot{q}$ for the momentum,

$$\boxed{qp - pq = i\hbar}. \tag{2.3}$$

For the corresponding three-dimensional problem, one has

$$H = \tfrac{1}{2}m(\dot{q}_1{}^2 + \dot{q}_2{}^2 + \dot{q}_3{}^2) + V(q_1, q_2, q_3),$$

where q_1, q_2 and q_3 are the 3 co-ordinates. It can be assumed, on physical grounds, that the 3 co-ordinates can be measured simultaneously, and that the 3 velocities can also be measured simultaneously, i.e., that

$$q_\alpha q_\beta = q_\beta q_\alpha, \qquad (\alpha, \ \beta = 1, \ 2, \ 3)$$

$$\dot{q}_\alpha \dot{q}_\beta = \dot{q}_\beta \dot{q}_\alpha.$$

Then the relation

$$q_\alpha H - H q_\alpha = i\hbar \dot{q}_\alpha$$

is satisfied, provided

$$m(q_\alpha \dot{q}_\beta - \dot{q}_\beta q_\alpha) = i\hbar \delta_{\alpha\beta} = \begin{cases} 1, \ \alpha = \beta, \\ 0, \ \alpha \neq \beta. \end{cases}$$

Thus, if $p_\alpha = m\dot{q}_\alpha$,

$$\boxed{\begin{aligned} q_\alpha q_\beta = q_\beta q_\alpha, \quad p_\alpha p_\beta = p_\beta p_\alpha, \\ q_\alpha p_\beta - p_\beta q_\alpha = i\hbar \delta_{\alpha\beta} \end{aligned}} \tag{2.4}$$

For a system of several particles, the energy has the form

$$H = \Sigma_r \tfrac{1}{2} m_r \dot{q}_r^2 + V(q_1, q_2, \ldots)$$

and the commutation rules are similar. If $p_r = m\dot{q}_r$, one has

$$\boxed{\begin{aligned} q_r q_s = q_s q_r, \quad p_r p_s = p_s p_r, \\ q_r p_s - p_s q_r = i\hbar \delta_{rs} \end{aligned}} \tag{2.5}$$

2.5 Other Commutators

If

$$qp - pq = i\hbar,$$

one finds

$$q^2 p - p q^2 = q(qp - pq) + (qp - pq)q$$
$$= i\hbar q + i\hbar q = 2i\hbar q,$$
$$q^3 p - p q^3 = q(q^2 p - p q^2) + (qp - pq)q^2$$
$$= 2i\hbar q^2 + i\hbar q^2 = 3i\hbar q^2$$

and, by induction,

$$q^n p - p q^n = n i\hbar q^{n-1}.$$

Defining the derivative of a function $f(q)$ of a matrix argument q by

$$f'(q) = \lim_{\varepsilon \to 0} \varepsilon^{-1} \{ f(q + \varepsilon 1) - f(q) \},$$

one sees that

$$\boxed{f(q)p - pf(q) = i\hbar f'(q)}, \tag{2.6}$$

if $f(q)$ is any polynomial in q, or any matrix function which can be developed in a power series in q.

By multiplying $qp - pq = i\hbar$ by q^{-1} before and after, one finds

$$q^{-1}(qp - pq)q^{-1} = i\hbar q^{-2},$$

and hence

$$q^{-1}p - pq^{-1} = -i\hbar q^{-2},$$

also

$$q^{-n}p - pq^{-n} = -ni\hbar q^{-(n+1)}.$$

Thus the result proved above is extended to functions which can be expanded in inverse powers of q. If c is any constant,

$$(q - c)p - p(q - c) = i\hbar,$$

so the same is true of functions which can be expanded in positive and negative powers of $q - c$, and thus for all analytic functions.

2.6 Equations of Motion

Consider a particle with the Hamiltonian energy

$$H = p^2/(2m) + V(q),$$

where $qp - pq = i\hbar$. We verify that

$$\dot{q} = (qH - Hq)/(i\hbar) = p/m.$$

Also

$$\begin{aligned}
\dot{p} &= (pH - Hp)/(i\hbar) \\
&= [pV(q) - V(q)p]/(i\hbar) \\
&= -V'(q).
\end{aligned}$$

In spite of the formal resemblance between this equation and the classical equation of motion, the conclusions of the classical theory are not supported by matrix mechanics, except as an approximation under certain conditions. For what one actually measures are the eigenvalues of observables, and the eigen-

38

values of operators do not satisfy all the same equations as the operators themselves. If Planck's constant $\hbar$ is negligible compared with the total action involved in a mechanical problem, however, the commutation rule $qp-pq = i\hbar$ may be replaced by $qp = pq$ with small error. Then all the operators commute, and satisfy the same equations as their eigenvalues. Thus, in macroscopic systems, where the total action is always very large compared with $\hbar$, the application of classical mechanics is not in question. In atomic systems, however, results based on classical mechanics can only be right 'by accident'.

Ex. 7: If q_r, p_r are observables representing the co-ordinates and canonical momenta of a system of particles show that, if $f = f(q_1, q_2, \ldots)$ is an analytic function of the q's only,

$$fp_r - p_r f = i\hbar \frac{\partial f}{\partial q_r}$$

and that, if

$$H = \Sigma_r \, p_r{}^2/(2m_r) + V(q_1, \, q_2, \, \ldots),$$

the 'equations of motion' of classical theory are satisfied by the observables.

EXAMPLES II

1. Formulate a clear statement of the difference between uncertainty and indeterminacy. Consider a radio-active nucleus imbedded in a photographic emulsion, and surrounded by counters which record the emission of a β-particle if the nucleus decays. After some time the emulsion is removed; then developed; then scrutinized; then the counters are examined. At what stage, if any, did it become (a) determinate and (b) certain that the nucleus had either (i) decayed or (ii) not decayed?
2. Discuss the difficulties which might be encountered in obtaining accurate values of the displacement and velocity of a particle under the following circumstances: (1) in a cloud chamber with a magnetic field, where the track of the particle is used to determine its position and the curvature of the track is used to determine its momentum; (2) in an arrangement where the particle passes through tiny holes in two screens, and

39

counters in delayed coincidence are placed near the holes to measure the time required for the particle to travel between them.

Under (1) discuss the effect of the density of the gas in the cloud chamber and the strength of the magnetic field; under (2) discuss the effect, if any, of the diameter of the holes and the distance between the screens.

3. In what circumstances is it possible to predict with certainty the result of an experiment? What does it mean to say that the probability of a particular result has a certain value? A particle with known momentum is allowed to collide with another particle, and then enters a magnetic field in a cloud chamber, which is, however, not operated. At what stages is it possible to speak of the probability that the particle has momentum within certain limits?

4. In quantum mechanics, how do we represent the possible results of a measurement, and the state of a system on which the measurement is made? What is an observable? What is the condition that two different measurements should be compatible? What is it that determines the probability that a measurement will yield a particular result? Summarize the physical interpretation of quantum mechanics.

5. What is the physical basis for believing that energy and momentum are conserved at the atomic level? Summarize the Hamiltonian formulation, and the Lagrangian formulation of classical mechanics, and show that they both imply conservation of energy and momentum, except under certain conditions which should be carefully stated. What is wrong with Hamiltonian and Lagrangian mechanics; how does this affect the validity of the conservation laws?

6. Assuming the commutation rule

$$AH - HA = i\hbar \frac{dA}{dt},$$

(where H is the Hamiltonian operator), and that

$$\psi^{(f)} * A \psi^{(i)} = \text{constant} \times e^{-i\omega t},$$

where $\psi^{(i)}$ and $\psi^{(f)}$ are vectors representing the initial and final states of an atom, and ω is the angular frequency of the radiation emitted, prove that the energy of the radiation emitted is $\hbar\omega$. If U is the operator

$$U = \exp(-iHt/\hbar),$$

and

$$\psi_s^{(i)} = U\psi^{(i)}, \qquad A_s = UAU^*,$$

show that

$$i\hbar \frac{d\psi_s^{(i)}}{dt} = H\psi_s^{(i)}, \qquad \frac{dA_s}{dt} = 0.$$

7. If $H = \frac{1}{2}m\dot{q}^2 + V(q^2)$, show that the commutation rules for the energy are satisfied provided

$$qp - pq = i\hbar(1+2l),$$

where $p = m\dot{q}$ and $lp + pl = 0$. Prove that $lq + ql$ anti-commutes with p, and does not depend on the time, provided l does not depend on the time.

8. One meaning of the additional 'solution' of the commutation rules obtained in 7 can be understood as follows: Let $\sigma_1{}^2 = \sigma_2{}^2 = 1$ and $\sigma_3 = -i\sigma_1\sigma_2 = i\sigma_2\sigma_1$. Also let $q = (q_1, q_2, q_3)$ be the position vector and $p = (p_1, p_2, p_3)$ be the momentum of a particle. We then have, according to the ordinary commutation rules,

$$q_\alpha p_\beta - p_\beta q_\alpha = i\hbar\delta_{\alpha\beta},$$

and we assume that each σ_α commutes with all the q_α and p_α. Let us now define

$$q = \mathbf{q} \cdot \boldsymbol{\sigma} = q_1\sigma_1 + q_2\sigma_2 + q_3\sigma_3,$$
$$p = \mathbf{p} \cdot \boldsymbol{\sigma} = p_1\sigma_1 + p_2\sigma_2 + p_3\sigma_3,$$
$$l\hbar = (\mathbf{q} \times \mathbf{p}) \cdot \boldsymbol{\sigma} + \hbar = (q_2 p_3 - q_3 p_2)\sigma_1 + (q_3 p_1 - q_1 p_3)\sigma_2$$
$$+ (q_1 p_2 - q_2 p_1)\sigma_3 + \hbar.$$

Prove that

$$qp - pq = i\hbar(1+2l),$$
$$ql + lq = pl + lp = 0,$$
$$q^2 = \mathbf{q}^2, \quad p^2 = \mathbf{p}^2.$$

9. Show that
$$qp^n - p^n q = ni\hbar p^{n-1},$$

and hence
$$q\, e^{-iap/\hbar} - e^{-iap/\hbar}\, q = ae^{-iap/\hbar},$$

i.e.,
$$e^{iap/\hbar}\, qe^{-iap/\hbar} = q+a.$$

Thus the unitary transformation effected with the operator $e^{iap/\hbar}$ has the effect of displacing a particle from the point q to the point $q+a$.

10. Write down the Hamiltonian of two particles, whose mutual potential energy $V(r)$ depends only on the distance r, which satisfies $r^2 = \mathbf{r}^2 = r_1^2 + r_2^2 + r_3^2$, where $\mathbf{r} = \mathbf{q}_1 - \mathbf{q}_2$ is the relative displacement of the two particles. If m_1 and m_2 are the masses of the particles, and
$$\mathbf{p}_r = (m_1\mathbf{p}_2 - m_2\mathbf{p}_1)/(m_1+m_2),$$
show that
$$r_\alpha p_{r\beta} - p_{r\beta} r_\alpha = i\hbar\delta_{\alpha\beta};$$

also, if $\mathbf{x} = (m_1\mathbf{q}_1 + m_2\mathbf{q}_2)/(m_1+m_2)$ and $\mathbf{p}_x = \mathbf{p}_1 + \mathbf{p}_2$, then
$$x_\alpha p_{x\beta} - p_{x\beta} x_\alpha = i\hbar\delta_{\alpha\beta},$$
$$x_\alpha p_{r\beta} = p_{r\beta} x_\alpha, \qquad r_\alpha p_{x\beta} = p_{x\beta} r_\alpha.$$

Also, show that
$$H = \tfrac{1}{2}\mathbf{p}_x^2/(m_1+m_2) + \tfrac{1}{2}(m_1+m_2)\mathbf{p}_r^2/(m_1 m_2) + V(r).$$

What is the significance of this decomposition?

3. The Simple Harmonic Oscillator

Simple harmonic oscillations occur rather widely in atomic physics. In a diatomic molecule, for example, the relative motion of the two atoms is harmonic to a good approximation, provided the amplitude of the oscillations is not too large. The same is true of the relative motion of the atoms in more complex molecules. The motion of the atoms or ions in a crystal can be resolved into a large number of simple harmonic motions. Finally, as we shall see later, electromagnetic radiation is equivalent to a system of harmonic oscillators, two for each frequency.

The Hamiltonian energy of a linear oscillator is of the form

$$H = p^2/(2m) + cq^2.$$

The problem which has to be solved is to determine the eigenvalues of this observable, which are called the *energy levels* of the oscillator. These are uniquely determined by the above formula for the energy, and the commutation rule $qp - pq = i\hbar$. To simplify the problem, let

$$\omega^2 = 2c/m,$$

so that ω is the angular frequency of the oscillations in the classical theory, and set

$$p = (m\hbar\omega)^{\frac{1}{2}} P,$$

$$q = (\hbar\omega/2c)^{\frac{1}{2}} Q,$$

so that

$$H = \tfrac{1}{2}(P^2 + Q^2)\hbar\omega \tag{3.1}$$

and

$$qp - pq = (m\hbar^2\omega^2/2c)^{\frac{1}{2}}(QP - PQ)$$
$$= \hbar(QP - PQ).$$

Thus

$$QP - PQ = i. \tag{3.2}$$

It is required to find the eigenvalues of the operator $\frac{1}{2}(P^2+Q^2)$. There is a general method for doing this, which will be explained later. To begin with, we shall just write down the solution.

3.1 Solution of the Problem

Consider the infinite matrix $[A_{kl}]$ defined by

$$A_{kl} = \begin{cases} 0, l \neq k+1 \\ \alpha k^{\frac{1}{2}}, l = k+1 \end{cases}$$

(where α is a complex number of modulus 1) for $k, l = 1, 2, 3, \ldots$ Its hermitean conjugate is the matrix A_{kl}^* with

$$A_{kl}^* = \begin{cases} 0, k \neq l+1 \\ \alpha^* l^{\frac{1}{2}}, k = l+1 \end{cases}$$

where α^* is the complex conjugate of α, and $\alpha\alpha^* = 1$.
   Explicitly

$$A = \alpha \begin{bmatrix} 0 & 1 & 0 & 0 & : \\ 0 & 0 & 2^{\frac{1}{2}} & 0 & : \\ 0 & 0 & 0 & 3^{\frac{1}{2}} & : \\ & & \cdots & & : \end{bmatrix} \quad , \quad A^* = \alpha^* \begin{bmatrix} 0 & 0 & 0 & : \\ 1 & 0 & 0 & : \\ 0 & 2^{\frac{1}{2}} & 0 & : \\ 0 & 0 & 3^{\frac{1}{2}} & : \\ & \cdots & & \end{bmatrix} .$$

By straight-forward multiplication,

$$AA^* = \begin{bmatrix} 1 & 0 & 0 & : \\ 0 & 2 & 0 & : \\ 0 & 0 & 3 & : \\ & \cdots & & : \end{bmatrix} \quad , \quad A^*A = \begin{bmatrix} 0 & 0 & 0 & 0 & : \\ 0 & 1 & 0 & 0 & : \\ 0 & 0 & 2 & 0 & : \\ & & \cdots & & : \end{bmatrix} .$$

Thus, $AA^* - A^*A = 1$.
   Then, if

$$A = (Q+iP)/2^{\frac{1}{2}}, \qquad A^* = (Q-iP)/2^{\frac{1}{2}},$$

one has

$$AA^* = \tfrac{1}{2}(Q^2+P^2) - \tfrac{1}{2}i(QP-PQ),$$
$$A^*A = \tfrac{1}{2}(Q^2+P^2) + \tfrac{1}{2}i(QP-PQ)$$

and, by subtraction,

$$QP-PQ = i,$$

44

as required by (3.2) above. Thus, if

$$Q = (A + A^*)/2^{\frac{1}{2}},$$
$$P = i(A^* - A)/2^{\frac{1}{2}},$$

the commutation rule is automatically satisfied. It is worth noticing that Q and P, defined in this way, are both hermitean, and therefore qualify as observables. Also

$$\tfrac{1}{2}(AA^* + A^*A) = \tfrac{1}{2}(P^2 + Q^2)$$

$$= \begin{bmatrix} \tfrac{1}{2} & 0 & 0 & 0 & \vdots \\ 0 & \tfrac{3}{2} & 0 & 0 & \vdots \\ 0 & 0 & \tfrac{5}{2} & 0 & \vdots \\ 0 & 0 & 0 & \tfrac{7}{2} & \vdots \\ & & \cdots & & \vdots \end{bmatrix}.$$

From this formula it can be seen that the eigenvalues of $\tfrac{1}{2}(P^2 + Q^2)$ are $\tfrac{1}{2}, \tfrac{3}{2}, \tfrac{5}{2}$, etc., and, in the representation chosen, the eigenvector corresponding to the eigenvalue $\tfrac{1}{2}(2j-1)$ is the vector $\psi^{(j)}$ with components $\psi_k{}^{(j)} = \delta_{jk}$.

The energy levels of the harmonic oscillator, i.e., the eigenvalues of H, defined in (3.1) above, are therefore

$$E^{(j)} = \tfrac{1}{2}(2j-1)\hbar\omega,$$

where j is a positive integer, and ω is the angular frequency of the classical theory. The measurement of the energy is bound to yield one of these eigenvalues. Thus energy can be gained and lost by the oscillator only in integral multiples of the interval $\hbar\omega$ between successive levels. Also, the state of lowest energy of the oscillator has energy $\tfrac{1}{2}\hbar\omega$, not zero as in the classical theory.

The complex number α appearing in the definition of A is arbitrary, so far as the determination of the eigenvalues is concerned, but is needed to satisfy the commutation rule

$$AH - HA = i\hbar\dot{A},$$

postulated by Heisenberg. As $H = (A^*A + \tfrac{1}{2})\hbar\omega$,

$$AH - HA = (AA^* - A^*A)A\hbar\omega$$
$$= A\hbar\omega.$$

So we must have $i\dot{A} = \omega A$, i.e., $i\dot{\alpha} = \omega\alpha$.

This is satisfied by

$$\alpha = \exp\left[-i\omega(t-t_0)\right],$$

where t_0 is arbitrary. If one is only concerned with observables at a particular time t_0, one can set $\alpha = 1$; but it must be remembered that observables which are not constants of the motion vary with the time.

Ex. 8: If $N = A^*A$, show that the eigenvalues of N are $0, 1, 2, \ldots$, and prove by induction that

$$(A^*)^n A^n = N(N-1)\ldots(N-n+1)$$

for positive integral values of n.

3.2 Deductive Method

To solve the same problem without knowing the answer, one would first try to express the observable $\frac{1}{2}(P^2+Q^2)$ whose eigenvalues are required in the form

$$\frac{1}{2}(P^2+Q^2) = A^*A + c_1, \tag{3.3}$$

where c_1 is a number. There are usually several ways of doing this: in this instance, two. If $A = (Q-iP)/2^{\frac{1}{2}}$, one finds, with the use of the commutation rule $QP-PQ = i$, that $c_1 = -\frac{1}{2}$; if $A = (Q+iP)/2^{\frac{1}{2}}$, one finds that $c_1 = \frac{1}{2}$. Quite generally, one selects the alternative which gives the largest value of c_1; in this instance, $A = (Q+iP)/2^{\frac{1}{2}}$.

Let ψ be any eigenvector of $N = A^*A$, and let λ be the corresponding eigenvalue, so that $N\psi = \lambda\psi$. Also, let $\phi^{(n)} = A^n\psi$. Then

$$\phi^{(n)*}\phi^{(n)} = (A^n\psi)^*A^n\psi$$
$$= \psi^*(A^*)^n A^n\psi.$$

Now, from the commutation rule $QP-PQ = i$, it follows that $AA^* - A^*A = 1$, and hence, according to Ex. 8, that

$$(A^*)^n A^n = N(N-1)\ldots(N-n+1).$$

By substitution in the above it follows that

$$\phi^{(n)*}\phi^{(n)} = \lambda(\lambda-1) \ldots (\lambda-n+1)\psi^*\psi$$
$$= \lambda(\lambda-1) \ldots (\lambda-n+1),$$

if ψ is properly normalized. But, if $\phi_k{}^{(n)}$ $(k = 1, 2, 3, \ldots)$ are the components of $\phi^{(n)}$,

$$\phi^{(n)*}\phi^{(n)} = \Sigma_k \phi_k{}^{(n)*}\phi_k{}^{(n)} \geq 0,$$

so

$$\boxed{\lambda(\lambda-1) \ldots (\lambda-n+1) \geq 0} \tag{3.4}$$

This inequality, which is valid for $n = 1, 2, 3, \ldots$, completely determines the eigenvalues of N, in much the same way as the equation $D(\lambda) = 0$ determines the eigenvalues of a finite matrix. For $n = 1$, it reduces to $\lambda \geq 0$, showing that N has no negative eigenvalues. For $n = 2$, the inequality states $\lambda(\lambda-1) \geq 0$; from this one sees that λ cannot have any value less than 1, except zero. For $n = 3$, one has $\lambda(\lambda-1)(\lambda-2) \geq 0$, showing that λ cannot have any value less than 2, except 0 and 1. Proceeding in this way, one finds that λ must be a non-negative integer. The eigenvalues of N are therefore $0, 1, 2, \ldots$, Since $c_1 = \frac{1}{2}$, one sees from (3.3) that the eigenvalues of $\frac{1}{2}(P^2+Q^2)$ are $\frac{1}{2}, \frac{3}{2}, \frac{5}{2}$, as already found in 3.1.

Another problem is to determine matrices which satisfy the required relations; this can be done as follows.

Let $\psi^{(1)}$ be the normalized eigenvector corresponding to the lowest eigenvalue $\lambda = 0$, so that $N\psi^{(1)} = 0$. All other eigenvectors can be expressed in terms of $\psi^{(1)}$, as we shall now show. Since $AA^* = N+1$,

$$NA^* = A^*AA^* = A^*(N+1)$$

and

$$N(A^*\psi^{(1)}) = A^*(N+1)\psi^{(1)} = A^*\psi^{(1)};$$

thus, $A^*\psi^{(1)}$ is an eigenvector of N, corresponding to the eigenvalue $\lambda = 1$. Also,

$$N(A^{*2}\psi^{(1)}) = A^*(N+1)(A^*\psi^{(1)}) = 2A^{*2}\psi^{(1)},$$

showing that $A^{*2}\psi^{(1)}$ is an eigenvector of N, corresponding to the eigenvalue $\lambda = 2$. Quite generally, the application of the operator $A*$ to an eigenvector produces another eigenvector with an eigenvalue increased by 1. Thus $A*^n\psi^{(1)}$ is an eigenvector, corresponding to the eigenvalue $\lambda = n$.

To normalize these eigenvectors, we note that $AA* = N+1$,

$$A^2A*^2 = A(A*A+1)A*$$
$$= AA*(AA*+1)$$
$$= (N+1)(N+2)$$

and, by induction,

$$A^nA*^n = (N+1)(N+2)\ldots(N+n).$$

Therefore

$$(A*^n\psi^{(1)})*A*^n\psi^{(1)} = \psi^{(1)}*A^nA*^n\psi^{(1)}$$
$$= \psi^{(1)}*(N+1)(N+2)\ldots(N+n)\psi^{(1)}$$
$$= n!\psi^{(1)}*\psi^{(1)} = n!,$$

if $\psi^{(1)}$ is normalized; and, if α is any complex number of modulus 1,

$$\psi^{(n+1)} = \alpha^n(n!)^{-\frac{1}{2}}A*^n\psi^{(1)}$$

will be a correctly normalized eigenvector, corresponding to the eigenvalue $\lambda = n$.

Since the $\psi^{(j)}$ are eigenvectors of a hermitean operator, they are orthogonal to one another and satisfy

$$\psi^{(j)}*\psi^{(k)} = \delta_{jk}.$$

One can therefore adopt a representation in which $\psi^{(j)}$ has the $\psi_l^{(j)} = \delta_{jl}$, and define the matrix elements of A by

$$A_{kl} = \psi^{(k)}*A\psi^{(l)}$$
$$= (A*\psi^{(k)})*\psi^{(l)}.$$

Now, from the formula (5) above one has

$$A*\psi^{(k)} = \alpha*k^{\frac{1}{2}}\psi^{(k+1)},$$

so that

$$A_{kl} = \alpha k^{\frac{1}{2}}\psi^{(k+1)}*\psi^{(l)} = \begin{cases} \alpha k^{\frac{1}{2}}, & l = k+1, \\ 0, & l \neq k+1, \end{cases}$$

in agreement with 3.1.

Ex. 9: (a) Show that, if c is an arbitrary number, the vector

48

ψ with components $\psi_k = c^{k-1} \left[(k-1)!\right]^{-\frac{1}{2}} e^{-c^2}$ is an eigenvector of A, and find the corresponding eigenvalue.

(b) If $f(n)$ is a function defined for integral values of n, show that

$$Af(N) = f(N+1)A \quad \text{and} \quad A^*f(N) = f(N-1)A^*.$$

3.3 *Average Values and Fluctuations*

Suppose we have an oscillator in the eigenstate with energy $(j-\frac{1}{2})\hbar\omega$ for which the normalized eigenvector is $\psi^{(j)}$. In **3.1** the representation was chosen in which the energy is represented by a diagonal matrix, and as a result, the components $\psi_k^{(j)} (=\delta_{jk})$ of an energy eigenvector were all zero except one (the j-th), which had the value 1. The average value of any observable L in the eigenstate considered is then $\psi^{(j)*}L\psi^{(j)} = L_{jj}$.

For instance, the average value of the observable $Q = (A+A^*)/\sqrt{2}$ is zero, since $A_{jj} = (A^*)_{jj} = 0$ and the average value of $P = i(A^*-A)/\sqrt{2}$ is also zero; this is, of course, what one would expect. Let us, however, calculate the average values of

$$Q^2 = \tfrac{1}{2}(A^2+A^{*2}+AA^*+A^*A),$$
$$P^2 = \tfrac{1}{2}(-A^2-A^{*2}+AA^*+A^*A).$$

Since

$$A^2 = \alpha^2 \begin{bmatrix} 0 & 0 & \sqrt{2} & 0 & : \\ 0 & 0 & 0 & \sqrt{6} & : \\ 0 & 0 & 0 & 0 & : \\ \cdots & \cdots & \cdots & \cdots \end{bmatrix}, \quad A^{*2} = \alpha^{*2} \begin{bmatrix} 0 & 0 & 0 & : \\ 0 & 0 & 0 & : \\ \sqrt{2} & 0 & 0 & : \\ 0 & \sqrt{6} & 0 & : \\ \cdots & \cdots & \cdots \end{bmatrix},$$

we see that $(A^2)_{jj} = (A^{*2})_{jj} = 0$. From the formulae already given, however, $(AA^*)_{jj} = j$ and $(A^*A)_{jj} = j-1$. So

$$(Q^2)_{jj} = (P^2)_{jj} = \tfrac{1}{2}(2j-1).$$

The mean square fluctuation in the position of the particle is therefore

$$(\varDelta q)^2 = (q^2)_{jj} = (\hbar\omega/2c)(j-\tfrac{1}{2})$$

and the mean square fluctuation in the momentum is

$$(\varDelta p)^2 = (p^2)_{jj} = m\hbar\omega(j-\tfrac{1}{2}).$$

49

Thus

$$(\Delta p \Delta q)^2 = (m\hbar^2\omega^2/2c)(j-\tfrac{1}{2})^2 = \hbar^2(j-\tfrac{1}{2})^2,$$
$$\Delta p \Delta q = (j-\tfrac{1}{2})\hbar.$$

Even in the ground state, i.e., the state of lowest energy, neither Δp nor Δq is zero ($\Delta p \Delta q = \tfrac{1}{2}\hbar$), as might be expected from the fact that the energy $\tfrac{1}{2}\hbar\omega$ is not zero either. This 'zero-point' energy cannot be taken from the oscillator, and is important in some applications.

3.4 Applications

It is easy to extend the above theory to oscillators with several, or many degrees of freedom. The energy reduces to the form

$$H = \Sigma_r \tfrac{1}{2}m_r \dot{q}_r^2 + \Sigma_r c_r q_r^2.$$

If one writes

$$H_r = \tfrac{1}{2}m_r \dot{q}_r^2 + c_r q_r^2,$$

so that $H = \Sigma_r H_r$, one can see from the commutation rules (2.5) that the H_r all commute with one another. They therefore have simultaneous eigenvalues and eigenvectors, and the energy levels are $\Sigma_r(j_r-\tfrac{1}{2})\hbar\omega_r$, where $\omega_r^2 = 2c_r/m_r$ and j_r is the quantum number associated with the r-th normal mode. The zero-point energy is $\tfrac{1}{2}\hbar\Sigma_r \omega_r$.

In constructing matrices to represent the various operators, one is faced with the problem of representing a set of operators A_r and their hermitean conjugates, so that $A_r A_r^* - A_r^* A_r = 1$, but $A_r A_s = A_s A_r$ and $A_r A_s^* = A_s^* A_r$ when $s = r$. This is most easily solved by writing

$$A_1 = A \times 1 \times 1 \times \ldots, \qquad A_1^* = A^* \times 1 \times 1 \times \ldots,$$
$$A_2 = 1 \times A \times 1 \times \ldots, \qquad A_2^* = 1 \times A^* \times 1 \times \ldots,$$
$$A_3 = 1 \times 1 \times A \times 1 \times \ldots, \text{ etc.,}$$

where $\times$ signifies the direct product. The matrix elements are, for instance,

$$(A_1)_{k_1 k_2 k_3 \cdots l_1 l_2 l_3} \cdots = A_{k_1 l_1} \delta_{k_2 l_2} \delta_{k_3 l_3} \cdots$$

when A_{kl} are the elements of the simple matrix A already found.

Ex. 10: If the energy of an oscillator in 2 dimensions has the form

$$H = \tfrac{1}{2}m(\dot{q}_1{}^2 + \dot{q}_2{}^2) + c_1 q_1{}^2 + 2c q_1 q_2 + c_2 q_2{}^2,$$

where $c_1 > 0$ and $c_1 c_2 > c^2$, show that it is reduced to normal form by the substitution

$$q_1 = q_a \cos\theta + q_b \sin\theta,$$
$$q_2 = q_b \cos\theta - q_a \sin\theta,$$

where $\tan 2\theta = 2c/(c_2 - c_1)$; and determine the energy levels.

(i) Atomic vibrations

Consider a diatomic molecule, for which the potential energy of the two atoms at distance r is $V(r)$. If $\mathbf{q}_1$ and $\mathbf{q}_2$ are co-ordinate vectors of the two atoms, r is defined as the principal square root of the operator $(\mathbf{q}_1 - \mathbf{q}_2)^2$, i.e., the square root has no negative eigenvalues and commutes with all observables which commute with $r^2 = (\mathbf{q}_1 - \mathbf{q}_2)^2$. Just as in classical mechanics, the energy of the diatomic molecule can be split up into the energy of translation H_{trans}, the energy of rotation H_{rot} and the energy of vibration H_{vib}:

$$H_{\text{vib}} = p_r{}^2/(2m) + V(r),$$

p_r is the component of the relative momentum where r points along the axis joining the two atoms, and m is the reduced mass. The momentum p_r is conjugate to the co-ordinate r and therefore satisfies $r p_r - p_r r = i\hbar$.

We shall suppose here that the resultant momentum, and the angular momentum of the molecule about its mass centre are both zero (strictly, that the molecule is in a state for which the momentum and angular momentum have zero eigenvalues), so that H_{trans} and H_{rot} are both zero and $H = H_{\text{vib}}$.

The potential energy function of two atoms which can form a molecule always has a minimum at the distance a, which in classical mechanics would be the point of equilibrium. Thus $V'(r) = 0$ for $r = a\mathbf{1}$. The expansion of $V(r)$ about $r = a\mathbf{1}$ is therefore

$$V(r) = V(a)\,\mathbf{1} + \tfrac{1}{2}V''(a)(r - a\mathbf{1})^2 + \cdots,$$

51

and if one neglects terms of order $(r-a1)^3$, one has

$$H = p_r^2/(2m) + \tfrac{1}{2}V''(a)(r-a1)^2 + V(a)1.$$

Since $(r-a1)p_r - p_r(r-a1) = i\hbar$, the theory already developed for the simple harmonic oscillator applies, and the energy levels are $V(a) + (j-\tfrac{1}{2})\hbar\omega$, where $\omega^2 = 2c/m = V''(a)/m$.

(ii) Radiation

We notice briefly also one of the most important applications, to the quantum theory of radiation. The energy density in an electromagnetic field is known, from Maxwell's theory, to be $\tfrac{1}{2}(\mathbf{E}^2 + \mathbf{B}^2)$, in Heaviside units, where $\mathbf{E}$ is the electric intensity and $\mathbf{B}$ is the magnetic induction. Thus the energy in a cube of volume $V = (2\pi)^3$ which contains no charge is

$$H = \tfrac{1}{2}\int_0^{2\pi}\int_0^{2\pi}\int_0^{2\pi} (\mathbf{E}^2 + \mathbf{B}^2)dx_1\,dx_2\,dx_3.$$

This can be worked out by expressing $\mathbf{E}$ and $\mathbf{B}$ in terms of the vector potential $\mathbf{A}$ of the field $(\mathbf{E} = -\dot{\mathbf{A}}/c$ and $\mathbf{B} = \mathrm{curl}\,\mathbf{A})$, and expanding $\mathbf{A}$ as a 3-dimensional Fourier series within the region of integration:

$$\mathbf{A} = \Sigma_\mathbf{n}\mathbf{q}(\mathbf{n})\,e^{i\mathbf{n}\cdot\mathbf{x}},$$

where $\mathbf{q}(-\mathbf{n}) = \mathbf{q}^*(\mathbf{n})$, since $\mathbf{A}$ is real. This leads to the development

$$H = \tfrac{1}{2}(V/c^2)\,\Sigma_\mathbf{n}\{\dot{\mathbf{q}}_R^2(\mathbf{n}) + \dot{\mathbf{q}}_I^2(\mathbf{n}) + c^2\mathbf{n}^2\mathbf{q}_R^2(\mathbf{n}) + c^2\mathbf{n}^2\mathbf{q}_I^2(\mathbf{n})\},$$

where $\mathbf{q}_R(\mathbf{n})$ and $\mathbf{q}_I(\mathbf{n})$ are the real and imaginary parts of $\mathbf{q}(\mathbf{n})$. The radiation field is therefore dynamically equivalent to a set of harmonic oscillators, one for each wave-vector $\mathbf{n}$ (two for the pair of wave-vectors $\mathbf{n}$ and $-\mathbf{n}$). The angular frequency of the oscillator corresponding to the wave vector $\mathbf{n}$ is $\omega(\mathbf{n}) = c|\mathbf{n}|$, and the energy levels of the oscillator are therefore $(j-\tfrac{1}{2})\hbar\omega(\mathbf{n})$. Thus energy can be gained or lost by the field only in units, or *quanta* of $\hbar\omega(\mathbf{n})$, where $\omega(\mathbf{n})$ is the angular frequency of the radiation concerned; and Planck's hypothesis of the discrete nature of radiation is confirmed.

Ex. 11: Try to fill in the details of the evaluation of the energy H above. It will be necessary to use the relation $\mathrm{div}\,\mathbf{A} = 0$ satisfied by the vector potential.

EXAMPLES III

1.   If $\theta = ap - ibq$, where $qp - pq = i\hbar$ and a and b are positive real numbers, and $H = a^2p^2 + b^2q^2$, prove that

$$\theta\theta^* = H + ab\hbar, \quad \theta^*\theta = H - ab\hbar,$$
$$\theta\theta^* = \theta^*\theta + 2ab\hbar, \quad \theta^2\theta^{*2} = (\theta^*\theta + 2ab\hbar)(\theta^*\theta + 4ab\hbar),$$
$$\theta^n\theta^{*n} = (\theta^*\theta + 2ab\hbar)(\theta^*\theta + 4ab\hbar) \ldots (\theta^*\theta + 2nab\hbar),$$
$$\theta^{*n+1}\theta^{n+1} = \theta^*\theta(\theta^*\theta - 2ab\hbar) \ldots (\theta^*\theta - 2nab\hbar).$$

Suppose ψ is a normalized eigenvector of $\theta^*\theta$ and λ is the corresponding eigenvalue: $\theta^*\theta\psi = \lambda\psi$, where $\psi^*\psi = 1$. If $\phi_n = \theta^n\psi$, show that $\phi_{n+1}^*\phi_{n+1} = \psi^*\theta^{*n+1}\theta^{n+1}\psi = \lambda(\lambda - 2ab\hbar)\ldots(\lambda - 2nab\hbar)$. From this deduce that

$$\lambda \geqq 0, \; \lambda(\lambda - 2ab\hbar) \geqq 0, \; \lambda(\lambda - 2ab\hbar)(\lambda - 4ab\hbar) \geqq 0,$$
$$\ldots \lambda(\lambda - 2ab\hbar) \ldots (\lambda - 2nab\hbar) \geqq c,$$

and that it is impossible for λ to have values *between* $2(n-1)ab$ and $2nab$, where n is any positive integer. What, then, are the eigenvalues of $\theta^*\theta$; of H?

2. With the same notation as in 1., suppose $H\psi_0 = ab\hbar\psi_0$, where $\psi_0^*\psi_0 = 1$. If $\psi_1 = \theta^*\psi_0$, show that $H\psi_1 = 3ab\hbar\psi_1$ and $\psi_1^*\psi_1 = 2ab\hbar$. If $H\psi_{n-1} = (2n-1)ab\hbar\psi_{n-1}$ and $\psi_n = \theta^*\psi_{n-1}$, show that $H\psi_n = (2n+1)ab\hbar\psi_n$ and $\psi_n^*\psi_n = 2nab\hbar\psi_{n-1}^*\psi_{n-1}$.

Deduce that $\psi_n^*\psi_n = n!(2ab\hbar)^n$, and that

$$\chi_n = \psi_n/[n!(2ab\hbar)^n]^{\frac{1}{2}}$$

is a normalized eigenvector of H.

3. With the notation of 1. and 2., prove that $\theta\psi_0 = 0$. Suppose χ is a vector which satisfies $p\chi = 0$; show that

$$\psi_0 = \exp\left[-\tfrac{1}{2}bq^2/(a\hbar)\right]\chi.$$

Note: in Schrödinger's wave mechanics, the commutation relation $qp - pq = i\hbar$ is satisfied by treating q as a real variable, and representing p as a differential operator:

$$p = -i\hbar(d/dq).$$

If we adopt this representation, the vector χ becomes a numerical constant, and ψ_0 is simply a function of q, as shown above.

4. With the same notation, show that

$$\psi_n*\theta*\psi_{n-1} = n!\,(2ab\hbar)^n,$$

and

$$\chi_n*\theta*\chi_{n-1} = (2ab\hbar n)^{\frac{1}{2}};$$

also, that $\psi_{n-1}^*\theta\psi_n = n!\,(2ab\hbar)^n$, and

$$\chi_{n+1}^*\theta\chi_n = (2ab\hbar n)^{\frac{1}{2}}.$$

Prove that $\psi_m*\psi_n = 0$, unless $m = n$. Deduce that $\psi_m*\theta*\psi_n = 0$, unless $m = n+1$. Prove also that $\psi_m*\theta\psi_n = 0$, unless $m = n-1$.

5. Show that $p = \frac{1}{2}(\theta+\theta*)/a$, and hence calculate $\chi_m*p\chi_n$ (i) for $m < n-1$; (ii) for $m = n-1$; (iii) for $m = n$; (iv) for $m = n+1$, and (v) for $m > n+1$. Calculate $\chi_m^*q\chi_n$ for all values of m and n.

6. The deuteron is a bound state of a neutron and a proton. The masses of these particles are almost equal; let us denote them by M. Their mutual potential energy at the distance r can be represented by the operator function $V(r) = -V \exp(-\beta^2r^2)$, where $r^2 = (\mathbf{q}_1-\mathbf{q}_2)^2$ and V is positive.

Since, within the deuteron, the distance between the particles is never large, we may use the approximation $V(r)=-V(1-\beta^2r^2)$. The Hamiltonian operator is then

$$H = (\mathbf{p}_1{}^2+\mathbf{p}_2{}^2)/(2M)-V+V\beta^2r^2.$$

Show that the binding energy of the deuteron is

$$V-3\beta\hbar(V/M)^{\frac{1}{2}},$$

in this approximation.

The following is more difficult. Suppose ψ is the eigenvector of the approximate Hamiltonian H. A more accurate value of the binding energy can be obtained by calculating

$$\psi*[(\mathbf{p}_1{}^2+\mathbf{p}_2{}^2)/2M-V\exp(-\beta^2r^2)]\psi.$$

7. Explain how average values are calculated in quantum mechanics. In the context of 6., find the mean kinetic energy of the two particles, their mean mutual potential energy, and the root mean square distance between them.

8. Investigate the representation of the electromagnetic field as a set of harmonic oscillators, in the following way. In the absence of charge or current, Maxwell's equations for the field are

$$\nabla \times \mathbf{E} = -\dot{\mathbf{B}}/c, \qquad \nabla \times \mathbf{B} = \dot{\mathbf{E}}/c,$$
$$\nabla \cdot \mathbf{E} = 0, \qquad \nabla \cdot \mathbf{B} = 0.$$

Show that these equations are satisfied by

$$\mathbf{B} = \nabla \times \mathbf{A}, \qquad \mathbf{E} = -\dot{\mathbf{A}}/c,$$

provided

$$\nabla \cdot \mathbf{A} = 0, \qquad \nabla^2 \mathbf{A} = \ddot{\mathbf{A}}/c^2.$$

Also, show that these last two equations are satisfied by the Fourier expansion

$$\mathbf{A} = \sum_{\mathbf{k}} \mathbf{q}(\mathbf{k})\, e^{i\mathbf{k} \cdot \mathbf{x}},$$

provided

$$\mathbf{k} \cdot \mathbf{q}(\mathbf{k}) = 0,$$

and the following harmonic oscillator equation is satisfied:

$$\ddot{\mathbf{q}}(\mathbf{k}) = -c^2 k^2 \mathbf{q}(\mathbf{k}).$$

9. The energy density of the electromagnetic field is $\frac{1}{2}(\mathbf{E}^2 + \mathbf{B}^2)$, in Heaviside units. The total energy in a rectangular region R is therefore

$$H = \frac{1}{2}\int_{R} (\mathbf{E}^2 + \mathbf{B}^2) d^3x.$$

Let us write

$$\mathbf{B} = \nabla \times \mathbf{A}, \qquad \mathbf{E} = -\dot{\mathbf{A}}/c,$$

and expand $\mathbf{A}$ in Fourier series within R, so that

$$\mathbf{A} = \sum_{\mathbf{k}} \mathbf{q}(\mathbf{k})\, e^{i\mathbf{k} \cdot \mathbf{x}}$$

and

$$V\mathbf{q}(\mathbf{k}) = \int_{R} \mathbf{A}\, e^{-i\mathbf{k} \cdot \mathbf{x}} d^3x,$$

where V is the volume of R, since

$$\int_{R} e^{i(\mathbf{k}-\mathbf{l}) \cdot \mathbf{x}} d^3x = \begin{cases} 0, & \mathbf{k} \neq \mathbf{l}, \\ V, & \mathbf{k} = \mathbf{l}. \end{cases}$$

Show that

$$\int \dot{\mathbf{A}}^2 d^3x = V\Sigma_{\mathbf{k}}\dot{\mathbf{q}}(\mathbf{k}) \cdot \dot{\mathbf{q}}(-\mathbf{k})$$

and

$$\int (\nabla \times \mathbf{A})^2 d^3x = V\Sigma_{\mathbf{k}} k^2 \mathbf{q}(\mathbf{k}) \cdot \mathbf{q}(-\mathbf{k}),$$

so that

$$H = \tfrac{1}{2}V \ \Sigma_{\mathbf{k}}[\dot{\mathbf{q}}(\mathbf{k}) \cdot \dot{\mathbf{q}}(-\mathbf{k})/c^2 + k^2 \ \mathbf{q}(\mathbf{k}) \cdot \mathbf{q}(-\mathbf{k})].$$

As $\mathbf{A}$ is real, $\mathbf{q}(-\mathbf{k})=[\mathbf{q}(\mathbf{k})]^*$.

Write $\mathbf{q}(\mathbf{k}) = \mathbf{q}_{R\mathbf{k}}+i\mathbf{q}_{I\mathbf{k}}$, and show that

$$H = \tfrac{1}{2}V\Sigma_{\mathbf{k}}[(\dot{\mathbf{q}}_{R\mathbf{k}}^2+\dot{\mathbf{q}}_{I\mathbf{k}}^2)/c^2 + k^2(\mathbf{q}_{R\mathbf{k}}^2+\mathbf{q}_{I\mathbf{k}}^2)].$$

This is the Hamiltonian of a set of harmonic oscillators; what are the energy levels?

10 Investigate the physical interpretation of the results obtained in 8. and 9. as follows. The state of lowest energy of the field is the vacuum. If one of the oscillators (associated with the 'coordinate' $\mathbf{q}_{R\mathbf{k}}$ or $\mathbf{q}_{I\mathbf{k}}$) is excited, a photon (of momentum $\hbar\mathbf{k}$ or $-\hbar\mathbf{k}$) is present. Suppose ψ_0 is the state vector of the vacuum. Show that $[\dot{\mathbf{q}}(\mathbf{k})-ick\mathbf{q}(\mathbf{k})]\psi_0$ is the unnormalized vector for the state with one proton, and find the corresponding normalized state vector, assuming that ψ_0 is already normalized.

4. General Results

In our study of the harmonic oscillator, some questions have arisen which deserve a more general discussion than was possible in the context. We shall now devote some attention to these questions in general.

4.1 Time Dependence of Operators

In writing down the formulae for A and A^* in 3.1, the time-dependence of the matrices was restricted to the factors α and α^*. In more complicated problems the time-dependence of the matrices can be much more complex, and we shall see how Heisenberg's equation

$$i\hbar \frac{dL}{dt} = LH - HL$$

can be satisfied. This equation can, in fact, be satisfied by the substitution

$$L = \exp(-i\hbar Ht)L_0 \exp(i\hbar Ht),$$

where L_0 is the value of L at the initial time $t = 0$. So, if one effects the canonical transformation

$$q \rightarrow q_0 = UqU^*,$$
$$p \rightarrow p_0 = UpU^*,$$

where $U = \exp(i\hbar Ht)$, the transformed co-ordinates and momenta become time-independent. On the other hand, a vector $\psi \rightarrow \psi_0 = U\psi$ becomes time-dependent. This transformation takes us to what is known as the Schrödinger representation.

It is usually convenient, in finding matrix representations, to determine the time-independent matrices representing q_0, p_0, etc. first and then use the known relation between q and q_0, p and p_0, etc., to calculate the time-dependent matrices. In a representation in which the energy is diagonal, this is particularly simple. For if $\psi^{(j)}$ and $\psi^{(k)}$ are normalized eigenvectors of H, and $E^{(j)}$ and $E^{(k)}$ are the corresponding eigenvalues,

$$L_{jk} = \psi^{(j)} {}^* L \psi^{(k)}$$
$$= \psi^{(j)} {}^* \exp\,(-i\hbar Ht)L_0 \exp\,(i\hbar Ht)\psi^{(k)}$$
$$= \exp\,\{-i\hbar(E^{(j)} - E^{(k)})t\}(L_0)_{jk}.$$

This is essentially a reversal of the argument by which Heisenberg's equation was obtained.

4.2 *Determination of Eigenvalues*

The method by which the eigenvalues of the operator $\frac{1}{2}(Q^2 + P^2)$ was determined in 3.2 is a general one which can be applied to any hermitean operator whose eigenvalues have a lower bound.

Suppose we wish to determine the eigenvalues of an operator A. We write $A_1 = A$ and express A_1 in the form

$$A_1 = \theta_1{}^* \theta_1 + a^{(1)},$$

where $a^{(1)}$ is a number. In case this can be done in more than one way, the way which yields the largest value of $a^{(1)}$ is chosen. Next, we define

$$A_2 = \theta_1 \theta_1{}^* + a^{(1)}$$

and try to express A_2 in the form

$$A_2 = \theta_2{}^* \theta_2 + a^{(2)}$$

which gives $a^{(2)}$ its greatest value; clearly $a^{(2)} \geqq a^{(1)}$.

Continuing this process, A_{j+1} is defined recursively by

$$A_{j+1} = \theta_j \theta_j{}^* + a^{(j)}$$

and θ_j and $a^{(j)}$ by

$$A_j = \theta_j{}^* \theta_j + a^{(j)}.$$

Then we shall show that $a^{(j)}$ is the j-th eigenvalue of A, in order of increasing magnitude.

Let ψ be any normalized eigenvector of A, and a the corresponding eigenvalue; and write

$$\phi^{(n)} = \theta_n \theta_{n-1} \ldots \theta_2 \theta_1 \psi.$$

Now

$$\phi^{(1)*}\phi^{(1)} = \psi^*\theta_1^*\theta_1\psi$$
$$= \psi^*(A_1 - a^{(1)})\psi$$
$$= (a - a^{(1)}),$$

since $A_1\psi = a\psi$ and $\psi^*\psi = 1$. Since $\phi^{(1)*}\phi^{(1)} \geq 0$, $a \geq a^{(1)}$; thus there is no eigenvalue less than $a^{(1)}$.

Before proceeding further, notice that

$$A_{j+1}\theta_j = (\theta_j\theta_j^* + a^{(j)})\theta_j$$
$$= \theta_j(\theta_j^*\theta_j + a^{(j)})$$
$$= \theta_j A_j.$$

Thus we have, for instance,

$$\phi^{(2)*}\phi^{(2)} = \psi^*\theta_1^*\theta_2^*\theta_2\theta_1\psi$$
$$= \psi^*\theta_1^*(A_2 - a^{(2)})\theta_1\psi$$
$$= \psi^*\theta_1^*\theta_1(A_1 - a^{(2)})\psi$$
$$= (a - a^{(2)})\phi^{(1)*}\phi^{(1)}$$
$$= (a - a^{(2)})(a - a^{(1)})$$

and $(a - a^{(2)})(a - a^{(1)}) \geq 0$. So $a \geq a^{(2)}$, unless $a = a^{(1)}$. Similarly,

$$\phi^{(n)*}\phi^{(n)} = \psi^*\theta_1^* \ldots \theta_{n-1}^*\theta_n^*\theta_n\theta_{n-1} \ldots \theta_1\psi$$
$$= \psi^*\theta_1^* \ldots \theta_{n-1}^*(A_n - a^{(n)})\theta_{n-1} \ldots \theta_1\psi$$
$$= \psi^*\theta_1^* \ldots \theta_{n-1}^*\theta_{n-1} \ldots \theta_1(A_1 - a^{(n)})\psi$$
$$= (a - a^{(n)})\phi^{(n-1)*}\phi^{(n-1)}.$$

Hence

$$\boxed{(a - a^{(n)})(a - a^{(n-1)}) \ldots (a - a^{(1)}) \geq 0.}$$

From this we deduce that either $a \geq a^{(n)}$, or $(a - a^{(n-1)}) \ldots (a - a^{(1)}) = 0$: the eigenvalues a must have one of the values $a^{(1)}, a^{(2)}, \ldots a^{(n)}$, or be greater than any of them. As this is true for all n, and $a^{(j+1)} \geq a^{(j)}$, a must have one of the values $a^{(j)}$, if the sequence $a^{(1)}, a^{(2)}, \ldots$ is unbounded. If the sequence $a^{(1)}, a^{(2)}, \ldots$ is bounded, with the upper bound $a^{(\max)}$, a may have one of the values $a^{(j)}$, or it may have an unrestricted value not less than $a^{(\text{max})}$. In either event, the eigenvalues of A are completely determined.

The above analysis is also frequently useful in determining the corresponding eigenvectors. Supposing that $\psi^{(j)}$ was the eigenvector corresponding to the eigenvalue $a^{(j)}$, $\phi^{(j-1)*}\phi^{(j-1)} > 0$, but $\phi^{(j)*}\phi^{(j)} = 0$, so $\phi^{(j)} = 0$, i.e., $\theta_j\phi^{(j-1)} = 0$. Therefore

$$(A_j - a^{(j)})\phi^{(j-1)} = \theta_j^*\theta_j\phi^{(j-1)} = 0,$$

showing that $\phi^{(j-1)}$ is an eigenvector of A_j, and $a^{(j)}$ the corresponding eigenvalue. Hence, if

$$\boxed{\psi^{(j)} = \theta_1^*\theta_2^* \dots \theta_{j-1}^* \phi^{(j-1)},}$$

we have, using $A_j\theta_j^* = \theta_j^*A_{j+1}$,

$$A\psi^{(j)} = \theta_1^*\theta_2^* \dots \theta^*_{j-1}A_j\phi^{(j-1)}$$
$$= a^{(j)}\psi^{(j)}.$$

This shows that if the vector $\phi^{(j-1)}$ satisfying $\theta_j\phi^{(j-1)} = 0$ is first determined, the above formula for $\psi^{(j)}$ yields the eigenvector of A corresponding to the eigenvalue $a^{(j)}$.

In the application of the above method to the harmonic oscillator, $\theta_j = (Q+iP)/2^{\frac{1}{2}}$ for all values of j.

4.3 *A Derivation of Schrödinger's Equation*

Suppose one wishes to find the eigenvalues of the energy H for a particle in a field of potential $V(q)$:

$$H = p^2/(2m) + V(q).$$

Let

$$A = 2mH = p^2 + 2mV(q).$$

The lowest eigenvalue $a^{(1)}$ of A is found by expressing A in the form

$$A = [p - if(q)][p + if(q)] + a^{(1)}$$

in such a way that $a^{(1)}$ has its greatest value.

60

Comparing the two formulae for A, one sees that they are equivalent, provided

$$2mV(q) = [f(q)]^2 - i[f(q)p - pf(q)] + a^{(1)}$$
$$= [f(q)]^2 + \hbar f'(q) + a^{(1)},$$

where the prime signifies differentiation.

Let $f = \hbar \Psi'/\Psi$ so that $f' = \hbar \Psi''/\Psi - \hbar(\Psi'/\Psi)^2$; then the above relation reduces to

$$2mV = \hbar^2 \Psi''/\Psi + a^{(1)}, \text{ i.e.,}$$
$$(-\hbar^2 \Psi'' + 2mV\Psi) = a^{(1)}\Psi,$$

which is Schrödinger's equation for the same problem. In Schrödinger's method, the eigenvalue always appears as the eigenvalue of a differential operator.

The reader who is already familiar with wave mechanics will know, however, that Schrödinger's equation is not sufficient in itself to determine the eigenvalues. It is often postulated, in addition, that Ψ, regarded as a function of the co-ordinate, should be finite, continuous and single-valued. Actually these conditions, as stated, are too *strong*; they are sufficient, but not necessary, and sometimes exclude admissible eigenvalues. It is necessary and sufficient to require that $|\Psi|^2$, regarded as a function of the co-ordinates, should be integrable and single-valued. These conditions may be called the *weak* conditions needed to determine eigenvalues from Schrödinger's equation.

The weak conditions, but not the strong conditions, of wave mechanics are implicit in matrix mechanics. In matrix mechanics it is required that the length $\psi^*\psi$ of any vector ψ should be finite. Schrödinger's equation can be obtained from

$$(p^2 + 2mV)\psi = a^{(1)}\psi$$

by adopting a representation $\psi = \Psi(q)$ of ψ in function space and the corresponding representation $p = -i\hbar(d/dq)$ for p. With this representation,

$$\psi^*\psi = \int |\Psi|^2 dq,$$

so that, if $\psi^*\psi$ is finite, the integral will also exist.

Ex. 12: Determine the eigenvalues of the operator $A = p^2 + 2cq^{-1}$ by assuming $\theta_k = p + i(a_k + b_k q^{-1})$, where a_k and b_k are real. (Answer: $a^{(j)} = -(c/j\hbar)^2$, where j is an integer, or $a \geqq 0$). Discuss the application of this result to the energy levels of a hydrogen atom, assuming the momentum and angular momentum of the atom are both zero.

4.4 Heisenberg's Indeterminacy Principle

We saw in 3.3 that the root mean square fluctuation in the co-ordinate of an oscillator (Δq) and the root mean square fluctuation in its momentum (Δp) satisfied the equation $\Delta p \Delta q = \frac{1}{2}\hbar$ in the ground state. We shall now show that the root mean square fluctuations of *any* co-ordinate q and its conjugate momentum p must satisfy the inequality $\Delta p \Delta q \geqq \frac{1}{2}\hbar$.

Let ψ be any normalized vector; the mean values of q and p in the state represented by ψ are

$$\langle q \rangle = \psi^* q \psi, \qquad \langle p \rangle = \psi^* p \psi.$$

The mean square fluctuations in the co-ordinate and momentum are given by

$$(\Delta q)^2 = \psi^* (q - \langle q \rangle)^2 \psi,$$
$$(\Delta p)^2 = \psi^* (p - \langle p \rangle)^2 \psi.$$

Let

$$B = q - \langle q \rangle + ic(p - \langle p \rangle),$$

where c is real; then

$$(B\psi)^* (B\psi) = \psi^* B^* B \psi$$
$$= \psi^* [(q - \langle q \rangle)^2 + c^2 (p - \langle p \rangle)^2 + ic(qp - pq)]\psi$$
$$= (\Delta q)^2 + c^2 (\Delta p)^2 - c\hbar.$$

But $(B\psi)^* (B\psi) \geqq 0$; hence (assuming that $c > 0$),

$$c^{-1}(\Delta q)^2 + c(\Delta p)^2 \geqq \hbar.$$

Now, when Δq and Δp are kept fixed, but c is allowed to vary, the left-hand side of this inequality has its minimum value for

$$-c^{-2}(\Delta q)^2 + (\Delta p)^2 = 0,$$

i.e., $c = \Delta q / \Delta p$. For this value of c, the inequality reduces to $2\Delta q \Delta p \geq \hbar$, i.e., $\Delta q \Delta p \geq \frac{1}{2}\hbar$. (Thus, in the ground state of the oscillator, $\Delta q \Delta p$ has its absolute minimum).

The above inequality, discovered by Heisenberg, shows that the indeterminacy Δp in the momentum must increase as the indeterminacy Δq in the co-ordinate decreases, and conversely. So — if quantum mechanics is right — there is no hope of ever making simultaneous measurements of two observables q and p with more than a certain accuracy.

4.5 *External and Internal Degrees of Freedom*

We mentioned in 3.4 (i) that the energy of a diatomic molecule could be split up, as in classical mechanics, into energies of translation, rotation and vibration. We shall now see in more detail how this is done.

Suppose, to begin with, the energy is expressed in the form

$$H = p_1^2/(2m_1) + p_2^2/(2m_2) + V(r),$$

where $r = (\mathbf{q}^2)^{\frac{1}{2}}$, when $\mathbf{q} = \mathbf{q}_1 - \mathbf{q}_2$. To split off the translational energy, we write

$$\mathbf{P} = \mathbf{p}_1 + \mathbf{p}_2, \qquad M = m_1 + m_2,$$

$$\mathbf{p} = (m_2\mathbf{p}_1 - m_1\mathbf{p}_2)/(m_1 + m_2), \qquad m = m_1 m_2/(m_1 + m_2),$$

so that m is the *reduced* mass; then

$$\mathbf{p}_1^2/(2m_1) + \mathbf{p}_2^2/(2m_2) = \mathbf{P}^2/(2M) + \mathbf{p}^2/(2m),$$

where $\mathbf{P}^2/(2M)$ is obviously what has been called H_{trans}, the energy of translation. Since $\mathbf{P}$ commutes with $\mathbf{p}$ and $\mathbf{q}$, and therefore with r, the term $\mathbf{P}^2/(2M)$ can be treated as an ordinary number in the Hamiltonian; its eigenvalues must obviously be positive, but are otherwise unrestricted.

The term $\mathbf{p}^2/(2m)$ obviously represents the kinetic energy of the internal degrees of freedom, and must be split further into rotational and vibrational kinetic energies. We first note that

$$q_\alpha p_\beta - p_\beta q_\alpha = \frac{[m_2(q_{1\alpha}p_{1\beta} - p_{1\beta}q_{1\alpha}) + m_1(q_{2\alpha}p_{2\beta} - p_{2\beta}q_{2\alpha})]}{(m_1 + m_2)}$$

$$= i\hbar \delta_{\alpha\beta},$$

so that $\mathbf{q}$ and $\mathbf{p}$ are canonically conjugate, as the notation suggests. The momentum p_r conjugate to r is defined by

$$rp_r = \mathbf{q} \cdot \mathbf{p} - i\hbar, \tag{4.1}$$

the term $-i\hbar$ being included to make p_r hermitean.

Ex. 13: Prove that (a) $\mathbf{q} \cdot \mathbf{p} - \mathbf{p} \cdot \mathbf{q} = 3i\hbar$;
(b) $(q^2)^{-1}\mathbf{p} - \mathbf{p}(q^2)^{-1} = -2i\hbar\mathbf{q}/(q^2)^2$;
(c) $\mathbf{q} \wedge \mathbf{p} + \mathbf{p} \wedge \mathbf{q} = 0$;
(d) $\mathbf{q}^2\mathbf{p} = \mathbf{q}\mathbf{q} \cdot \mathbf{p} - \mathbf{q} \wedge (\mathbf{q} \wedge \mathbf{p})$

We have to prove that (i) $rp_r - p_r r = i\hbar$ and (ii) $p_r{}^* = p_r$. The first follows straight forwardly from (4.1):
$rp_r - p_r r = r^{-1}(r\mathbf{q} \cdot \mathbf{p} - \mathbf{q} . \mathbf{p}r) = i\hbar$, since $r\mathbf{p} - \mathbf{p}r = i\hbar\mathbf{q}/r$.
To prove the second, take the hermitean conjugate of (4.1), using the formula $(AB)^* = B^*A^*$; then

$p_r{}^*r = \mathbf{p} \cdot \mathbf{q} + i\hbar = (\mathbf{q} \cdot \mathbf{p} - 3i\hbar) + i\hbar = rp_r - i\hbar = p_r r$, so $p_r{}^* = p_r$.

We wish to show, finally, that

$$\mathbf{p}^2 = p_r{}^2 + r^{-2}\mathbf{L}^2, \tag{4.2}$$

where $\mathbf{L} = \mathbf{q} \wedge \mathbf{p}$ is the angular momentum about the mass centre. To do this, we split $\mathbf{p}$ into components parallel and perpendicular to $\mathbf{q}$, using the vector formula

$$\mathbf{p} = (\mathbf{q}^2)^{-1}[\mathbf{q}\mathbf{q} \cdot \mathbf{p} - \mathbf{q} \wedge (\mathbf{q} \wedge \mathbf{p})],$$

and form the scalar product with $\mathbf{p}$ from the left:

$$\mathbf{p}^2 = \mathbf{p} \cdot \{(q^2)^{-1}[\mathbf{q}\mathbf{q} \cdot \mathbf{p} - \mathbf{q} \wedge (\mathbf{q} \wedge \mathbf{p})]\}.$$

Now

$$\mathbf{p}(q^2)^{-1} = (q^2)^{-1}(\mathbf{p} + 2i\hbar\mathbf{q}/q^2),$$

so this gives

$$\mathbf{p}^2 = (q^2)^{-1}[\mathbf{p} \cdot \mathbf{q}\,\mathbf{q} \cdot \mathbf{p} + 2i\hbar\mathbf{q} \cdot \mathbf{p} - (\mathbf{p} \wedge \mathbf{q}) \cdot (\mathbf{q} \wedge \mathbf{p})]$$
$$= r^{-2}[(\mathbf{q} \cdot \mathbf{p} - i\hbar)\mathbf{q} \cdot \mathbf{p} + \mathbf{L}^2],$$

since $\mathbf{p} \wedge \mathbf{q} = -\mathbf{q} \wedge \mathbf{p}$. Now

$$r^{-2}(\mathbf{q} \cdot \mathbf{p} - i\hbar)\mathbf{q} \cdot \mathbf{p} = r^{-1}p_r(rp_r + i\hbar)$$
$$= r^{-1}(rp_r - i\hbar)p_r + i\hbar r^{-1}p_r$$
$$= p_r{}^2,$$

so that (4.2) is verified. The term $r^{-2}\mathbf{L}^2/(2m)$ is obviously the energy of rotation H_{rot}, and we have therefore reduced the energy to the form

$$H = H_{\text{trans}} + H_{\text{rot}} + (p_r^2/2m) + V(r)$$

which was assumed in 3.4.

4.6 Eigenvalues of the Angular Momentum

The result (4.2) which was proved in 4.5,

$$\mathbf{p}^2 = p_r^2 + r^{-2}\mathbf{L}^2,$$

and the determination of the eigenvalues of

$$H = \mathbf{p}^2/(2m) + c\mathbf{r}^2$$

by the method of 3.4 provide an indirect but simple means of finding the eigenvalues of $\mathbf{L}^2$. Suppose

$$\mathbf{L}^2\psi^{(k)} = \lambda^{(k)}\psi^{(k)},$$

so that $\psi^{(k)}$ is an eigenvector of $\mathbf{L}^2$ and $\lambda^{(k)}$ is the corresponding eigenvalue. Since each component of $\mathbf{L} = \mathbf{q} \wedge \mathbf{p}$ commutes with $\mathbf{r}^2, \mathbf{p}^2$, and therefore also with p_r^2, $\mathbf{L}^2$ commutes with H. Therefore $\psi^{(k)}$ can be expressed in terms of common eigenvectors $\psi^{(jk)}$ of H and $\mathbf{L}^2$:

$$\psi^{(k)} = \sum_j c_j \psi^{(jk)},$$

$$\mathbf{L}^2\psi^{(jk)} = \lambda^{(k)}\psi^{(jk)},$$

and

$$2mH\psi^{(jk)} = (p_r^2 + r^{-2}\mathbf{L}^2 + 2mcr^2)\psi^{(jk)}$$

$$= (p_r^2 + \lambda^{(k)}r^{-2} + 2mcr^2)\psi^{(jk)}$$

$$= a^{(j)}\psi^{(jk)}, \text{ say.}$$

Now, the eigenvalues of H are already known from 3.4; they are

$$[(j_1 - \tfrac{1}{2}) + (j_2 - \tfrac{1}{2}) + (j_3 - \tfrac{1}{2})]\hbar\omega,$$

where $\omega^2 = 2c/m$. Hence

$$a^{(j)} = 2m(l^{(j)} + \tfrac{3}{2})\hbar(2c/m)^{\frac{1}{2}}$$

$$= (2l^{(j)} + 3)(2mc)^{\frac{1}{2}}\hbar,$$

65

where $l^{(j)} = j_1+j_2+j_3-3$ takes the values 0, 1, 2, ... But if

$$\theta_1 = p_r+ikr^{-1}-i(2mc)^{\frac{1}{2}}r,$$

we find

$$\theta_1{}^*\theta_1 = p_r{}^2+[kr^{-1}-(2mc)^{\frac{1}{2}}r]^2-k\hbar r^{-2}-(2mc)^{\frac{1}{2}}\hbar$$
$$= 2mH-a^{(1)},$$

provided

$$k(k-\hbar) = \lambda^{(k)},$$
$$a^{(1)} = (2mc)^{\frac{1}{2}}(2k+\hbar)$$
$$= (2mc)^{\frac{1}{2}}(2l^{(1)}+3)\hbar.$$

Hence

$$k = (l^{(1)}+1)\hbar,$$
$$\lambda^{(k)} = l^{(1)}(l^{(1)}+1)\hbar^2.$$

The eigenvalues of $\mathbf{L}^2$ are therefore of the form $l(l+1)\hbar^2$, where l takes the values 0, 1, 2, ...

This result will be confirmed by a more direct method in the next chapter.

EXAMPLES IV

1. Let us define $\langle A\rangle = \psi^*A\psi$, $\langle B\rangle = \psi^*B\psi$,

$$\Delta A = [\psi^*(A-\langle A\rangle)^2\psi]^{\frac{1}{2}}, \quad \Delta B = [\psi^*(B-\langle B\rangle)^2\psi]^{\frac{1}{2}}$$

and $C = -i(AB-BA)$ for any pair of hermitean operators A and B. Let $\phi = [A-\langle A\rangle+i\alpha(B-\langle B\rangle)]\psi$, where α is a constant. Show that

$$\phi^*\phi = \Delta A^2+\alpha^2\Delta B^2-\alpha\langle C\rangle,$$

and hence that

$$\Delta A\Delta B \geqq \tfrac{1}{2}\langle C\rangle.$$

Prove also that $\Delta A\Delta B \geqq -\tfrac{1}{2}\langle C\rangle$. Show that, if $\Delta A\Delta B=\tfrac{1}{2}\langle C\rangle > 0$, then $\phi = 0$, and $[(\Delta B/\Delta A)(A-\langle A\rangle)^2+(\Delta A/\Delta B)(B-\langle B\rangle)^2]\psi = C\psi$. Deduce that $\Delta q\Delta p$ has its minimum value *only* if ψ is a harmonic oscillator state vector.

2. If $\mathbf{A}$, $\mathbf{B}$, $\mathbf{C}$ are arbitrary space vector operators, and the product $\mathbf{B}\times\mathbf{C}$ means the space vector operator with components $(\mathbf{B}\times\mathbf{C})_1 = B_2C_3-B_3C_2$, $(\mathbf{B}\times\mathbf{C})_2 = B_3C_1-B_1C_3$ and

$(\mathbf{B}\times\mathbf{C})_3 = B_1 C_2 - B_2 C_1$, show that $\mathbf{A}\cdot(\mathbf{B}\times\mathbf{C}) = (\mathbf{A}\times\mathbf{B})\cdot\mathbf{C}$ and $\mathbf{A}\times(\mathbf{B}\times\mathbf{C}) = \sum_\alpha A_\alpha \mathbf{B} C_\alpha - \mathbf{A}\cdot\mathbf{B} C$, i.e., $[\mathbf{A}\times(\mathbf{B}\times\mathbf{C})]_\beta = \sum_\alpha (A_\alpha B_\beta C_\alpha - A_\alpha B_\alpha C_\beta)$. Deduce that

$$\mathbf{p}\times(\mathbf{q}\times\mathbf{p}) = i\hbar\mathbf{p} + \mathbf{q}\mathbf{p}^2 - \mathbf{p}\mathbf{q}\cdot\mathbf{p}$$

and

$$(\mathbf{q}\times\mathbf{p})^2 = \mathbf{q}^2\mathbf{p}^2 - \mathbf{q}\cdot\mathbf{p}(\mathbf{q}\cdot\mathbf{p} - i\hbar).$$

3. Prove that $(\mathbf{q}\times\mathbf{p})^2$ commutes with $\mathbf{q}^2$ and $\mathbf{p}^2$. Show that if $q^2 = \mathbf{q}^2$ and $p = \mathbf{q}^{-1}(\mathbf{q}\cdot\mathbf{p} - i\hbar)$, then $p = (\mathbf{p}\cdot\mathbf{q} + i\hbar)q^{-1}$, so that $p^* = p$; also $qp - pq = i\hbar$ and $q^2 p^2 = \mathbf{q}\cdot\mathbf{p}(\mathbf{q}\cdot\mathbf{p} - \hbar i)$. Using the result of 2., deduce that

$$q^{-2}(\mathbf{q}\times\mathbf{p})^2 = \mathbf{p}^2 - p^2.$$

Hence show that, for a state of zero angular momentum $[(\mathbf{q}\times\mathbf{p})\psi = 0]$, $\mathbf{p}^2\psi = p^2\psi$.

4. If $A = p^2 - 2k\hbar q^{-1}$, where $qp - pq = i\hbar$ and k is a positive constant, show that

$$A = \theta_1^*\theta_1 - k^2,$$

where $\theta_1 = p + i\hbar q^{-1} - ik$, and

$$\theta_1\theta_1^* - k^2 = A + 2\hbar^2 q^{-2}.$$

If $A_n = A + n(n+1)\hbar^2 q^{-2}$ and

$$\theta_n = p + i\hbar n q^{-1} - ik/n,$$

show that

$$\theta_n\theta_n^* - k^2/n^2 = A_n = \theta_{n+1}^*\theta_{n+1} - k^2/(n+1)^2.$$

Deduce that $A_n\theta_n = \theta_n A_{n-1}$, and $A_1\theta_1 = \theta_1 A$.

5. With the notation of 4., show that if ψ is an eigenvector of A, and $\phi_n = \theta_n\theta_{n-1}\ldots\theta_2\theta_1\psi$, then $\phi_n^*\phi_n = (A + k^2)(A + k^2/4)\ldots(A + k^2/n^2)$. Hence show that, if ψ is a normalized eigenvector of A, and a is the corresponding eigenvalue, then

$$\phi_n^*\phi_n = (a + k^2)(a + k^2/4)\ldots(a + k^2/n^2).$$

From the fact that this expression cannot be negative, deduce that the only negative eigenvalues of A are $-k^2$, $-k^2/4$, $\ldots$, $-k^2/n^2$, $\ldots$

6. The total energy of the hydrogen atom is

$$H = \mathbf{p}_1^2/(2m_1) + \mathbf{p}_2^2/(2m_2) - e^2/(4\pi r),$$

where e is the electronic charge in Heaviside units and $r^2 = (\mathbf{q}_1 - \mathbf{q}_2)^2$. Verify that

$$H = (\mathbf{p}_1 + \mathbf{p}_2)^2/[2(m_1 + m_2)] + (\mathbf{r} \times \mathbf{p}_r)^2/r^2$$
$$+ p_r^2 - e^2/(4\pi r),$$

where $p_r = (m_1 \mathbf{p}_2 - m_2 \mathbf{p}_1)/(m_1 + m_2)$ and $r p_r = \mathbf{r} \cdot \mathbf{p}_r - i\hbar$. Hence deduce the energy levels of the S-states (states of zero angular momentum) when the centre of mass is at rest $[(\mathbf{p}_1 + \mathbf{p}_2)\psi = 0]$.

7. Using the notation of 5., show that if $a = -k^2/n^2$, $\phi_{n-1} \neq 0$, but $\theta_n \phi_{n-1} = 0$. If $A\psi_0 = -k^2\psi_0$ and $\psi_0^*\psi_0 = 1$, show that $\theta_1 \psi_0 = 0$, evaluate $\psi_0^*(q\theta_1 - \theta_1^*q)\psi_0$, $\psi_0^*(q^2\theta_1 - \theta_1^*q^2)\psi_0, \ldots$ $\psi_0^*(q^n\theta_1 - \theta_1^*q^n)\psi_0$ and hence show that $\langle q \rangle_0 = \psi_0^*q\psi_0 = 3\hbar/(2k)$, $\langle q^2 \rangle_0 = 12[\hbar/(2k)]^2, \ldots, \langle q^n \rangle_0 = \frac{1}{2}(n+2)![\hbar/(2k)]^n$.

8. With the notation of 7., evaluate $\psi_0^*(\theta_1 - \theta_1^*)\psi_0$ and hence show that $\langle q^{-1} \rangle_0 = \psi_0^*q^{-1}\psi_0 = k/\hbar$. Prove that $\langle p \rangle_0 = 0$ and $\langle p^2 \rangle_0 = k^2$. If

$$\Delta p = [\langle (p - \langle p \rangle_0)^2 \rangle_0]^{\frac{1}{2}} \text{ and } \Delta q = [\langle (q - \langle q \rangle_0)^2 \rangle_0]^{\frac{1}{2}},$$

show that $\Delta p \Delta q = \sqrt{3}\hbar/2$.

9. If $A = p^2 - a^2 \exp(-bq/\hbar)$, and $qp - pq = i\hbar$, where a and b are positive constants, show that, if $u = \exp(-\frac{1}{2}bq/\hbar)$,

$$A = \theta_1^*\theta_1 - b^2/16,$$

where $\theta_1 = p - iau \cot(2au/b) + \frac{1}{4}ib$. Investigate the eigenvalues of A.

10. The mutual potential energy $V(r)$ of the proton and the neutron in the deuteron can be represented by the formula

$$V(r) = -V \exp(-\frac{1}{2}br/\hbar).$$

Find the binding energy of the deuteron, assuming a pure S-state (no orbital angular momentum).

68

5. Angular Momentum

The angular momentum of any system, which is not subject to external forces, is a constant of the motion and may therefore be measured together with the total energy. However, as will be seen very soon, the three components of the angular momentum cannot be measured simultaneously; we can do no more than measure one of the components, and the resultant angular momentum.

Even before the discovery of matrix mechanics, Bohr realized that atomic spectra could only be explained if the angular momentum was limited to certain values, which are integral multiples of Planck's constant $\hbar$. But a full knowledge of the behaviour of the angular momentum of atomic systems was obtained only when matrix mechanics was developed.

The angular momentum of a particle is defined, as in classical mechanics, as a space vector $\mathbf{L} = \mathbf{q} \wedge \mathbf{p}$ with components

$$L_1 = q_2 p_3 - q_3 p_2, \quad L_2 = q_3 p_1 - q_1 p_3, \quad L_3 = q_1 p_2 - q_2 p_1,$$

where q_1, q_2, q_3 are the three co-ordinates of the particle and p_1, p_2, p_3 the corresponding components of the momentum. In classical mechanics, where co-ordinates and velocities can be measured simultaneously, co-ordinates and velocities are usually supposed to be measured relative to a non-physical, stationary origin. In quantum mechanics, the concept of a stationary point has to be discarded; but one can regard q_1, q_2, q_3 as the relative co-ordinates of two particles, and p_1, p_2, p_3 as the components of their relative momentum. If one of the particles is free of forces, it serves as a convenient origin, but should not be conceived as localized in space and motionless at the same time.

5.1 Commutation Rules

The commutation rules satisfied by the angular momentum

are easily worked out with the help of the rules

$$q_\alpha q_\beta = q_\beta q_\alpha, \qquad p_\alpha p_\beta = p_\beta p_\alpha,$$
$$q_\alpha p_\beta - p_\beta q_\alpha = i\hbar\delta_{\alpha\beta}.$$

For brevity we introduce the commonly used notation

$$[A,\ B] = AB - BA, \qquad\qquad (5.1)$$

so that the above rules, for instance, read $[q_\alpha,\ q_\beta] = [p_\alpha,\ p_\beta] = 0$; $[q_\alpha,\ p_\beta] = i\hbar\delta_{\alpha\beta}$.

The following identities are often useful:

$$[B,\ A] = -[A,\ B],$$
$$[A,\ BC] = [A,\ B]C + B[A,\ C],$$
$$[AB,\ C] = A[B,\ C] + [A,\ C]B.$$

From the definitions of L_1, L_2 and L_3 we find

$$
\begin{aligned}
[L_1,\ L_2] &= [q_2 p_3 - q_3 p_2,\ q_3 p_1 - q_1 p_3] \\
&= q_2[p_3,\ q_3]p_1 + p_2[q_3,\ p_3]q_1 \\
&= i\hbar(q_1 p_2 - q_2 p_1) = i\hbar L_3
\end{aligned}
$$

and, similarly, $[L_2,\ L_3] = i\hbar L_1$ and $[L_3,\ L_1] = i\hbar L_2$. These results may be summarized in space vector notation, thus

$$\boxed{\mathbf{L} \wedge \mathbf{L} = i\hbar\mathbf{L}}\ . \qquad\qquad (5.2)$$

(This shows, incidentally, that the vector rule $\mathbf{L} \wedge \mathbf{L} = 0$ does not always hold when the components of $\mathbf{L}$ are operators!) The fact that L_1 and L_2, for example, do not commute means that they are not simultaneously measurable. (There is a trivial exception: when the measured value of the resultant angular momentum is zero, i.e., when $\mathbf{L}^2$ has the eigenvalue zero, all the components have simultaneously the eigenvalue zero). However, we shall show that it is always possible to measure one component, L_3 say, and $\mathbf{L}^2$ simultaneously:

$$
\begin{aligned}
[L_3,\ L_1{}^2] &= [L_3,\ L_1]L_1 + L_1[L_3,\ L_1] \\
&= i\hbar(L_2 L_1 + L_1 L_2), \\
[L_3,\ L_2{}^2] &= [L_3,\ L_2]L_2 + L_2[L_3,\ L_2] \\
&= -i\hbar(L_1 L_2 + L_2 L_1).
\end{aligned}
$$

70

Adding these two results, together with $[L_3, L_3{}^2] = 0$, we find $[L_3, L_1{}^2+L_2{}^2+L_3{}^2] = 0$, i.e., $[L_3, \mathbf{L}^2] = 0$. By cyclic symmetry, it follows that

$$[L_\alpha, \mathbf{L}^2] = 0 \qquad (\alpha = 1,\ 2,\ 3).$$

We next obtain the commutators of the L_α with functions of $\mathbf{q}$ and $\mathbf{p}$. The results can be summarized in two Theorems:

THEOREM 1: If S is any scalar constructed from $\mathbf{q}$ and $\mathbf{p}$, $[L_\alpha, S] = 0$.

PROOF: Every scalar constructed from $\mathbf{q}$ and $\mathbf{p}$ is a function of $\mathbf{q}^2$, $\mathbf{p}^2$ and $\mathbf{q} \cdot \mathbf{p}$; so if the theorem is true for these 3 scalars, it will be true for every such scalar. Now, for $\mathbf{q}^2$, one has

$$[L_3,\ q_1\ ] = [q_1 p_2 - q_2 p_1,\ q_1] = -q_2[p_1,\ q_1] = i\hbar q_2,$$
$$[L_3,\ q_1{}^2] = [L_3,\ q_1]q_1 + q_1[L_3,\ q_1] = 2i\hbar q_1 q_2,$$
$$[L_3,\ q_2\ ] = [q_1 p_2 - q_2 p_1,\ q_2] = q_1[p_2,\ q_2] = -i\hbar q_1,$$
$$[L_3,\ q_2{}^2] = [L_3,\ q_2]q_2 + q_2[L_3,\ q_2] = -2i\hbar q_1 q_2,$$
$$[L_3,\ q_3\ ] = [q_1 p_2 - q_2 p_1,\ q_3] = 0,$$
$$[L_3,\ q_3{}^2] = 0.$$

So, by addition, $[L_3, \mathbf{q}^2] = 0$; and, by cyclic symmetry, $[L_\alpha, \mathbf{q}^2] = 0$.

To prove a similar result for $\mathbf{p}^2$, we notice that both the commutation rules and the components of the angular momentum are unchanged when we replace $\mathbf{q}$ by $i\mathbf{p}$ and $\mathbf{p}$ by $i\mathbf{q}$ simultaneously. If we make this replacement in the proof of $[L_\alpha, \mathbf{q}^2] = 0$, we obtain $[L_\alpha, \mathbf{p}^2] = 0$.

To prove a similar result for $\mathbf{p} \cdot \mathbf{q}$, we notice that both the commutation rules and the components of the angular momentum are unchanged when we replace $\mathbf{q}$ by $\frac{1}{2}(\mathbf{q}+\mathbf{p})$ and $\mathbf{p}$ by $\mathbf{p}-\mathbf{q}$ simultaneously. Making these replacements in the proof that $[L_\alpha, \mathbf{q}^2] = 0$, we obtain $[L_\alpha, (\mathbf{q}+\mathbf{p})^2] = 0$ and, since $[L_\alpha, \mathbf{q}^2] = [L_\alpha, \mathbf{p}^2] = 0$, we have $[L_\alpha, \mathbf{q} \cdot \mathbf{p}] = 0$. This result can of course also be obtained by direct calculation.

THEOREM 2: If $\mathbf{A}$ is any space vector constructed from $\mathbf{q}$ and $\mathbf{p}$,

$$[L_1, A_1] = [L_2, A_2] = [L_3, A_3] = 0,$$
$$[L_1, A_2] = [A_1, L_2] = i\hbar A_3,$$
$$[L_2, A_1] = [A_2, L_1] = -i\hbar A_3,$$
$$[L_2, A_3] = [A_2, L_3] = i\hbar A_1,$$
$$[L_3, A_2] = [A_3, L_2] = -i\hbar A_1,$$
$$[L_3, A_1] = [A_3, L_1] = i\hbar A_2,$$
$$[L_1, A_3] = [A_1, L_3] = -i\hbar A_2.$$

These results may be stated concisely by introducing the symbol $\varepsilon_{\alpha\beta\gamma}$ which has the value 0 when any two of the suffixes α, β, γ are equal, the value $+1$ when α, β, γ are an even (cyclic) permutation of 1, 2, 3, and the value -1 when α, β, γ are an odd permutation of 1, 2, 3. For then they may be written

$$[L_\alpha, A_\beta] = [A_\alpha, L_\beta] = i\hbar \Sigma_\gamma \varepsilon_{\alpha\beta\gamma} A_\gamma.$$

PROOF: It will be shown (i) that the theorem is true for $\mathbf{A} = \mathbf{q}$ and $\mathbf{A} = \mathbf{p}$; (ii) that if it is true for $\mathbf{A} = \mathbf{B}$ and $\mathbf{A} = \mathbf{C}$, it is true also for $S_b\mathbf{B} + S_c\mathbf{C}$, where S_b and S_c are scalars; (iii) that if it is true for $\mathbf{A} = \mathbf{B}$ and $\mathbf{A} = \mathbf{C}$, it is true for $\mathbf{A} = \mathbf{B} \wedge \mathbf{C}$.

(i): In the course of proving Theorem 1, we have shown that $[L_3, q_1] = i\hbar q_2$, $[L_3, q_2] = -i\hbar q_1$ and $[L_3, q_3] = 0$. It follows that $[q_1, L_3] = -i\hbar q_2$ and $[q_2, L_3] = i\hbar q_1$; thus all the relations involving L_3 are true when $\mathbf{A} = \mathbf{q}$, and by cyclic symmetry, those involving L_1 and L_2 are true also. Since the commutation rules and components of the angular momentum are unchanged when $\mathbf{q}$ is replaced by $i\mathbf{p}$ and $\mathbf{p}$ by $i\mathbf{q}$, Theorem 2 is true also when $\mathbf{A} = i\mathbf{p}$, and hence when $\mathbf{A} = \mathbf{p}$.

(ii): Since, if S_b and S_c are scalars constructed from $\mathbf{q}$ and $\mathbf{p}$, $[L_\alpha, S_b] = [L_\alpha, S_c] = 0$, $[L_\alpha, S_b\mathbf{B} + S_c\mathbf{C}] = S_b[L_\alpha, \mathbf{B}] + S_c[L_\alpha, \mathbf{C}]$. Thus, if Theorem 2 is true for $\mathbf{A} = \mathbf{B}$ and $\mathbf{A} = \mathbf{C}$, it is true also for $S_b\mathbf{B} + S_c\mathbf{C}$.

(iii) Again assuming the Theorem is true for $\mathbf{A} = \mathbf{B}$ and $\mathbf{A} = \mathbf{C}$, we have

$$\begin{aligned}
[L_3, (\mathbf{B} \wedge \mathbf{C})_1] &= [L_3, B_2C_3 - B_3C_2] \\
&= [L_3, B_2]C_3 - B_3[L_3, C_2] \\
&= -i\hbar B_1 C_3 + i\hbar B_3 C_1 \\
&= i\hbar (\mathbf{B} \wedge \mathbf{C})_2,
\end{aligned}$$

$$[L_3, \ (\mathbf{B} \wedge \mathbf{C})_2] = [L_3, B_3 C_1 - B_1 C_3]$$
$$= B_3[L_3, \ C_1] - [L_3, \ B_1]C_3$$
$$= i\hbar B_3 C_2 - i\hbar B_2 C_3$$
$$= -i\hbar (\mathbf{B} \wedge \mathbf{C})_1,$$
$$[L_3, \ (\mathbf{B} \wedge \mathbf{C})_3] = [L_3, \ B_1 C_2 - B_2 C_1]$$
$$= (i\hbar B_2)C_2 + B_1(-i\hbar C_1) - (-i\hbar B_1)C_1 - B_2(i\hbar C_2)$$
$$= 0.$$

The remainder of the results for $\mathbf{B} \wedge \mathbf{C}$ follow on using $[L_3, \ \mathbf{B} \wedge \mathbf{C}] = -[\mathbf{B} \wedge \mathbf{C}, \ L_3]$ and cyclic symmetry.

Ex. 12: Show that, if $\mathbf{A}$ is any space vector constructed from $\mathbf{q}$ and $\mathbf{p}$,
$$[\mathbf{L}^2, \ \mathbf{A}] = 2i\hbar(\mathbf{A} \wedge \mathbf{L} - i\hbar \mathbf{A});$$

and that, if $\mathbf{B} = \mathbf{A} \wedge \mathbf{L} - i\hbar \mathbf{A}$, $\mathbf{B}$ is hermitean and satisfies
$$[\mathbf{L}^2, \ \mathbf{B}] = 2i\hbar(\mathbf{A} \cdot \mathbf{L}\mathbf{L} - \mathbf{A}\mathbf{L}^2 - i\hbar \mathbf{B}).$$

5.2 *Angular Momentum of a System of Particles*

If we have a system of particles whose co-ordinate and momentum vectors are $\mathbf{q}^{(r)}$ and $\mathbf{p}^{(r)}$, the angular momentum of the system is $\mathbf{L} = \Sigma_r \mathbf{L}^{(r)}$, where $\mathbf{L}^{(r)} = \mathbf{q}^{(r)} \wedge \mathbf{p}^{(r)}$. Now, since $[q_\alpha^{(r)}, \ p_\beta^{(s)}] = 0$ when $r \neq s$, $[L_\alpha^{(s)}, \ L_\beta^{(s)}] = 0$ when $r \neq s$.

Hence
$$[L_\alpha, \ L_\beta] = \Sigma_r \Sigma_s [L_\alpha^{(r)}, \ L_\beta^{(s)}]$$
$$= \Sigma_r [L_\alpha^{(r)}, \ L_\beta^{(r)}]$$

and $[L_1, \ L_2] = \Sigma_r[L_1^{(r)}, \ L_2^{(r)}] = \Sigma_r(i\hbar L_3^{(r)}) = i\hbar L_3$. Similarly, $[L_2, \ L_3] = i\hbar L_1$ and $[L_3, \ L_1] = i\hbar L_2$. So the relation $\mathbf{L} \wedge \mathbf{L} = i\hbar \mathbf{L}$ holds for a system of particles, just as for a single particle. Also,
$$[L_\alpha, \ q_\beta^{(r)}] = \Sigma_s[L_\alpha^{(s)}, \ q_\beta^{(r)}]$$
$$= [L_\alpha^{(r)}, \ q_\beta^{(r)}];$$

so we have $[L_1, q_2^{(r)}] = i\hbar q_3^{(r)}$, etc.; and similarly $[L_1, p_2^{(r)}] = i\hbar p_3^{(r)}$, etc. We can therefore prove by induction theorems analogous to Theorems 1 and 2 of 5.1: (1), if S is any scalar constructed from the co-ordinates and momenta of the particles, it commutes with each component of the resultant angular momentum; also (2), if $\mathbf{A}$ is any space vector constructed from the co-ordinates and momenta of the particles,

$$[L_\alpha, A_\beta] = [A_\alpha, L_\beta] = i\hbar \Sigma_\gamma \varepsilon_{\alpha\beta\gamma} A_\gamma.$$

5.3 *Spin Matrices*

Some particles, in addition to their angular momentum about the origin, have what is known as spin angular momentum, which may be compared with the angular momentum of a rigid body about its mass centre. The spin angular momentum of a particle is denoted by the space vector $\mathbf{S}$; it does not depend on the co-ordinates or momenta of the particle, and it therefore commutes with $\mathbf{q}$, $\mathbf{p}$, and $\mathbf{L}$; but it satisfies the same equation $\mathbf{S} \wedge \mathbf{S} = i\hbar \mathbf{S}$ as $\mathbf{L}$.

Ex. 13: If $\mathbf{J} = \mathbf{L} + \mathbf{S}$, prove that $\mathbf{J} \wedge \mathbf{J} = i\hbar \mathbf{J}$.

The difference between $\mathbf{L}$ and $\mathbf{S}$ is that, for a particular kind of particle, $\mathbf{S}^2$ has only one eigenvalue, whereas $\mathbf{L}^2$ has infinitely many eigenvalues. The matrices representing $\mathbf{S}$ are therefore finite; those representing $\mathbf{L}$ are infinite. We shall therefore find it helpful to study the relatively simple spin matrices before the rather complicated matrices required to represent the angular momentum.

We first define a number s, called the *spin*: if the eigenvalue of $\mathbf{S}^2$ is λ, the non-negative number s satisfying $s(s+1)\hbar^2 = \lambda$ is called the spin.

SPIN ZERO: The equation $\mathbf{S} \wedge \mathbf{S} = i\hbar \mathbf{S}$ is satisfied in a trivial way by 'matrices' with one row and column, whose single element is zero. By taking $S_1 = S_2 = S_3 = [0]$, we find $\mathbf{S}^2 = [0]$; the eigenvalue of $\mathbf{S}^2$ is zero, and the spin is zero. The pion (π-meson) has spin zero.

SPIN HALF: The relation $\mathbf{S} \wedge \mathbf{S} = i\hbar \mathbf{S}$ can also be satisfied by matrices with two rows and columns. Let

$$\sigma_1 = \begin{pmatrix} 0 & 1 \\ 1 & 0 \end{pmatrix}, \qquad \sigma_3 = \begin{pmatrix} -1 & 0 \\ 0 & +1 \end{pmatrix},$$

then $\sigma_1{}^2 = \sigma_3{}^2 = 1$ and

$$\sigma_3\sigma_1 = -\sigma_1\sigma_3 = \begin{pmatrix} 0 & -1 \\ +1 & 0 \end{pmatrix}.$$

So, if we set $\sigma_2 = -i\sigma_3\sigma_1$, we have

$$\sigma_1\sigma_2 + \sigma_2\sigma_1 = -i(\sigma_1\sigma_3 + \sigma_3\sigma_1)\sigma_1 = 0,$$
$$\sigma_2\sigma_3 + \sigma_3\sigma_2 = -i\sigma_3(\sigma_1\sigma_3 + \sigma_3\sigma_1) = 0,$$
$$\sigma_2{}^2 = -(\sigma_3\sigma_1)^2 = \sigma_3\sigma_1{}^2\sigma_2 = \sigma_3{}^2 = 1.$$

These relations may be summarized in the form

$$\sigma_\alpha\sigma_\beta + \sigma_\beta\sigma_\alpha = 2\delta_{\alpha\beta}.$$

Also
$$\sigma_3\sigma_1 = i\sigma_2,$$
$$\sigma_1\sigma_2 = -i\sigma_1\sigma_3\sigma_1 = i\sigma_3\sigma_1{}^2 = i\sigma_3,$$
$$\sigma_2\sigma_3 = -i\sigma_3\sigma_1\sigma_3 = i\sigma_1\sigma_3{}^2 = i\sigma_1,$$

so

$$\sigma_\alpha\sigma_\beta = i\Sigma_\gamma \varepsilon_{\alpha\beta\gamma}\sigma_\gamma.$$

If, then, we define $\mathbf{S} = \tfrac{1}{2}\hbar\boldsymbol{\sigma}$, we find

$$S_1S_2 - S_2S_1 = \tfrac{1}{4}\hbar^2(\sigma_1\sigma_2 - \sigma_2\sigma_1)$$
$$= \tfrac{1}{2}i\hbar^2\sigma_3$$
$$= i\hbar S_3,$$

and similar relations by cyclic symmetry. So the relation $\mathbf{S} \wedge \mathbf{S} = i\hbar\mathbf{S}$ is satisfied by the matrices defined.

The σ-matrices (which are identical with the matrices iC, ii and C of 1.4) are called Pauli matrices, after W. Pauli, who first suggested their connection with the spin of the electron; sometimes also Clifford matrices, after Clifford who had investigated their mathematical properties in the 19th century. (Hamilton's *quaternions* are also really operators of the type $c_0 + i\mathbf{c} \cdot \boldsymbol{\sigma}$).

Since $\boldsymbol{\sigma}^2 = \sigma_1{}^2 + \sigma_2{}^2 + \sigma_3{}^2 = 3$, $\mathbf{S}^2 = 3\hbar^2/4 = \tfrac{1}{2}(\tfrac{1}{2}+1)\hbar^2$, showing that the spin, in this representation, is one half. Electrons, muons (μ-mesons), protons, neutrons, neutrinos and hyperons all have spin half.

Ex. 14: If $\mathbf{a}$ and $\mathbf{b}$ are numerical space vectors, show that $(\mathbf{a} \cdot \boldsymbol{\sigma})^2 = \mathbf{a}^2$ and $\mathbf{a} \cdot \boldsymbol{\sigma}\ \mathbf{b} \cdot \boldsymbol{\sigma} + \mathbf{b} \cdot \boldsymbol{\sigma}\ \mathbf{a} \cdot \boldsymbol{\sigma} = 2\mathbf{a} \cdot \mathbf{b}$. Show also that $\mathbf{a} \cdot \boldsymbol{\sigma}\ \mathbf{b} \cdot \boldsymbol{\sigma} = \mathbf{a} \cdot \mathbf{b} + i\mathbf{a} \wedge \mathbf{b} \cdot \boldsymbol{\sigma}$.

SPIN ONE: There is also a representation with **3** rows and columns, which has an application to the spin of the photon.

Let

$$\beta = \begin{pmatrix} 0 & 1 & 0 \\ 0 & 0 & 1 \\ 0 & 0 & 0 \end{pmatrix} \quad , \quad \beta^* = \begin{pmatrix} 0 & 0 & 0 \\ 1 & 0 & 0 \\ 0 & 1 & 0 \end{pmatrix} ,$$

so that

$$\beta\beta^* = \begin{pmatrix} 1 & 0 & 0 \\ 0 & 1 & 0 \\ 0 & 0 & 0 \end{pmatrix} \quad , \quad \beta^*\beta = \begin{pmatrix} 0 & 0 & 0 \\ 0 & 1 & 0 \\ 0 & 0 & 1 \end{pmatrix} .$$

Define β_3 by

$$\beta_3 = \beta^*\beta - \beta\beta^* = \begin{pmatrix} -1 & 0 & 0 \\ 0 & 0 & 0 \\ 0 & 0 & +1 \end{pmatrix} ,$$

so that

$$\beta\beta_3 = \begin{pmatrix} 0 & 0 & 0 \\ 0 & 0 & +1 \\ 0 & 0 & 0 \end{pmatrix} , \quad \beta_3\beta = \begin{pmatrix} 0 & -1 & 0 \\ 0 & 0 & 0 \\ 0 & 0 & 0 \end{pmatrix} ,$$

and $\beta\beta_3 - \beta_3\beta = \beta$. Taking the hermitean conjugate of this last relation [using $(AB)^* = B^*A^*$] we have also

$$\beta_3\beta^* - \beta^*\beta_3 = \beta^*.$$

Define also β_1 and β_2 by

$$\beta_1 = (\beta+\beta^*)/\sqrt{2}; \quad \beta_2 = i(\beta-\beta^*)/\sqrt{2}.$$

Then β_1 and β_2 are both hermitean and satisfy

$$\beta_1\beta_2 - \beta_2\beta_1 = i(\beta^*\beta - \beta\beta^*) = i\beta_3,$$
$$\beta_2\beta_3 - \beta_3\beta_2 = i[\beta, \beta_3]/\sqrt{2} - i[\beta^*, \beta_3]/\sqrt{2}$$
$$= i(\beta+\beta^*)/\sqrt{2} = i\beta_1,$$
$$\beta_3\beta_1 - \beta_1\beta_3 = [\beta_3, \beta]/\sqrt{2} + [\beta_3, \beta^*]/\sqrt{2}$$
$$= (-\beta+\beta^*)/\sqrt{2} = i\beta_2.$$

To summarize: $\boldsymbol{\beta} \wedge \boldsymbol{\beta} = i\boldsymbol{\beta}$; therefore, if we set $\mathbf{S} = \hbar\boldsymbol{\beta}$, we shall have $\mathbf{S} \wedge \mathbf{S} = i\hbar\mathbf{S}$.

To determine the spin, we compute

$$\beta_1{}^2+\beta_2{}^2 = \tfrac{1}{2}(\beta^2+\beta\beta^*+\beta^*\beta+\beta^{*2})+\tfrac{1}{2}(-\beta^2 \mid \beta\beta^* \mid \beta^*\beta \quad \beta^{*2})$$
$$= (\beta\beta^*+\beta^*\beta)$$
$$= 2-\beta_3{}^2.$$

Thus $\boldsymbol{\beta}^2 = 2$, and $\mathbf{S}^2 = 2\hbar^2 = s(s+1)\hbar^2$ where $s = 1$. These matrices therefore correspond to spin one.

Ex. 15: Prove that

$$\beta_\alpha\beta_\beta\beta_\gamma+\beta_\gamma\beta_\beta\beta_\alpha = \delta_{\alpha\beta}\beta_\gamma+\delta_{\beta\gamma}\beta_\alpha.$$

[First take all suffixes equal, then only two equal, finally all different.]

5.4 Angular Momentum Eigenvalues

We shall now determine the eigenvalues of the operators M_3 and $\mathbf{M}^2$, where $\mathbf{M}$ is any space vector satisfying $\mathbf{M} \wedge \mathbf{M} = i\hbar\mathbf{M}$. As we have already seen, this equation is satisfied by the orbital angular momentum $\mathbf{L}$, by the spin angular momentum $\mathbf{S}$, and (see Ex. 13) by $\mathbf{J} = \mathbf{L}+\mathbf{S}$. The theory will therefore apply to each of these.

Since $[M_\alpha,\ \mathbf{M}^2] = 0$, M_3 and $\mathbf{M}^2$ will have simultaneous eigenvalues; if ψ is a common eigenvector, assumed to be normalized, and $m_3\hbar$ and $m(m+1)\hbar^2$ are their respective eigenvalues,

$$M_3\psi = m_3\hbar\psi, \quad \mathbf{M}^2\psi = m(m+1)\hbar\psi. \tag{5.3}$$

It can be assumed that m is not negative. We shall show in this section that (a) m must be half an integer, i.e., it is either itself an integer (possibly zero) or half an odd integer; and (b) m_3 may take only the values $-m$, $-m+1$, $\ldots m$. Thus, m_3 is integral or half-odd-integral according as m is integral or half-odd-integral; and $|m_3| \leqq m$.

The method used to determine the eigenvalues is similar to that used for the harmonic oscillator, where use was made of the fact that $(A^n\psi)^*A^n\psi$ could not be negative. Here we shall use the fact that, if $M_+ = M_1+iM_2$ and $M_- = M_+{}^* = M_1-iM_2$,

$(M_+{}^n\psi)^*M_+{}^n\psi$ and $(M_-{}^n\gamma)^*M_-{}^n\psi$ cannot be negative. To evaluate these expressions we shall need the following results:

RESULT (1): If $f(M_3)$ is any polynomial function of M_3,

$$f(M_3)M_+ = M_+f(M_3+\hbar),$$
$$f(M_3)M_- = M_-f(M_3-\hbar).$$

As a corollary,

$$f(M_3)M_+{}^k = M_+{}^kf(M_3+k\hbar),$$
$$f(M_3)M_-{}^k = M_-{}^kf(M_3-k\hbar),$$

where k is any positive integer.

PROOF:

$$[M_3,\ M_+]=[M_3,\ M_1]+\mathrm{i}[M_3,\ M_2]$$
$$= \mathrm{i}\hbar M_2+\hbar M_1 = \hbar M_+,$$

so that $\qquad M_3M_+ = M_+(M_3+\hbar)$

and, by induction, $M_3{}^kM_+ = M_+(M_3+\hbar)^k$. It follows that, if $f(M_3)$ is any polynomial in M_3, $f(M_3)M_+ = M_+f(M_3+\hbar)$. Replacing $f(M_3)$ by $f^*(M_3-\hbar)$, we have $f^*(M_3-\hbar)M_+=M_+f^*(M_3)$. Taking the hermitean conjugate of this equation, and using $M_+{}^* = M_-$, we have, finally, $M_-f(M_3-\hbar) = f(M_3)M_-$.

RESULT (2): $M_-M_+ = \mathbf{M}^2-M_3(M_3+\hbar)$
and $\qquad\qquad M_+M_- = \mathbf{M}^2-M_3(M_3-\hbar)$.

PROOF:

$$M_-M_+ = (M_1-\mathrm{i}M_2)(M_1+\mathrm{i}M_2)$$
$$= M_1{}^2+M_2{}^2+\mathrm{i}[M_1,\ M_2]$$
$$= (\mathbf{M}^2-M_3{}^2)-\hbar M_3;$$
$$M_+M_- = (M_1+\mathrm{i}M_2)(M_1-\mathrm{i}M_2)$$
$$= M_1{}^2+M_2{}^2-\mathrm{i}[M_1,\ M_2]$$
$$= (\mathbf{M}^2-M_3{}^2)+\hbar M_3.$$

RESULT (3): $M_-{}^nM_+{}^n = \Pi_{k=1}^n\{\mathbf{M}^2-[M_3+(k-1)\hbar][M_3+k\hbar]\}$
and $\quad M_+{}^nM_-{}^n = \Pi_{k=1}^n\{\mathbf{M}^2-[M_3-(k-1)\hbar][M_3-k\hbar]\}$.

PROOF: By repeated application of

$$M_-^n M_+^n = M_-^{n-1}(M_- M_+)M_+^n \quad 1$$
$$= M_-^{n-1}[\mathbf{M}^2 - M_3(M_3 + \hbar)]M_+^{n-1}$$
$$= M_-^{n-1} M_+^{n-1}\{\mathbf{M}^2 - [M_3 + (n-1)\hbar][M_3 + n\hbar]\},$$

we obtain the first formula, and the second follows in a similar way from

$$M_+^n M_-^n = M_+^{n-1}(M_+ M_-)M_-^{n-1}$$
$$= M_+^{n-1}[\mathbf{M}^2 - M_3(M_3 - \hbar)]M_-^{n-1}$$
$$= M_+^{n-1} M_-^{n-1}\{\mathbf{M}^2 - [M_3 - (n-1)\hbar][M_3 - n\hbar]\}.$$

Now we are able to evaluate:

$$(M_+^n \psi)^* M_+^n \psi = \psi^* M_-^n M_+^n \psi$$
$$= \psi^* \Pi_{k=1}^n \{\mathbf{M}^2 - [M_3 + (k-1)\hbar][M_3 + k\hbar]\}\psi$$
$$= \Pi_{k=1}^n [m(m+1) - (m_3 + k - 1)(m_3 + k)]\hbar^2,$$

using (5.3) above and the normal condition $\psi^* \psi = 1$. Similarly,

$$(M_-^n \psi)^* M_-^n \psi = \Pi_{k=1}^n [m(m+1) - (m_3 - k + 1)(m_3 - k)]\hbar^2.$$

So we have

$$\Pi_{k=1}^n [m(m+1) - (m_3 + k - 1)(m_3 + k)] \geqq 0,$$
$$\Pi_{k=1}^n [m(m+1) - (m_3 - k + 1)(m_3 - k)] \geqq 0. \qquad (5.4)$$

Now when $m_3 + k - 1 > m$, $m(m+1) - (m_3 + k - 1)(m_3 + k) < 0$, and when $m_3 - k + 1 < -m$, $m(m+1) - (m_3 - k + 1)(m_3 - k) < 0$; so the inequalities (5.4) can only hold for all values of n if $m(m+1) = (m_3 + k - 1)(m_3 + k)$ for some positive integral value k_+ of k, and if $m(m+1) = (m_3 - k + 1)(m_3 - k)$ for some other positive integral value k_- of k_0. Hence

$$m = m_3 + k_+ - 1,$$
$$-m = m_3 - k_- + 1,$$

where k_+ and k_- are positive integers. By subtraction of these results, we see that $2m = k_+ + k_- - 2$; therefore $2m$ is a non-

79

negative integer. We see also that $m-m_3 = k_+-1 \geq 0$, and $m_3+m = k_- -1 \geq 0$; so $|m_3| \leq m$; also, m_3 differs from m by an integer.

Consider first the application of these results to the spin matrices. If $\mathbf{S}^2$ has the eigenvalue $s(s+1)\hbar^2$, s can only be an integer or half an odd integer; in 5.3, we studied the values 0, $\frac{1}{2}$ and 1, and it is possible (see 5.6) to construct also matrices corresponding to spins 3/2, 2, etc. For a particular value of s, there is a simultaneous eigenvalue $s_3\hbar$ of S_3 for $s_3 = -s$, $s_3 = -s+1, \ldots$ and $s_3 = s$. For example, as one can see from the explicit representations of 5.3, when $s = 0$, $s_3 = 0$; when $s = \frac{1}{2}$, $s_3 = -\frac{1}{2}$ or $\frac{1}{2}$; when $s = 1$, $s_3 = -1$, 0 or 1.

We can also conclude that, if $\mathbf{L}^2$ has the eigenvalue $l(l+1)\hbar^2$, there is a simultaneous eigenvalue $l_3\hbar$ of L_3 for $l_3 = -l$, $l_3 = -l+1, \ldots$ and $l_3 = l$. However, l can take only integral values, as we shall see in the next section.

5.5 Eigenvalues of the Orbital Angular Momentum

To prove that the eigenvalues of $\mathbf{L}^2$ are $l(l+1)\hbar^2$, where l takes only *integral* values, we make use of the relation

$$\mathbf{q} \cdot \mathbf{L} = q_1(q_2L_3-q_3L_2)+q_2(q_3L_1-q_1L_3)$$
$$+q_3(q_1L_2-q_2L_1) = 0.$$

(Incidentally, the wave-mechanical derivation of the eigenvalues of L_3 and $\mathbf{L}^2$, as presented in most text-books, is defective. It assumes that the wave-function Ψ must be single-valued, but on physical grounds only $|\Psi|^2$ need be single-valued.)

Using the relation $\mathbf{q} \cdot \mathbf{L} = 0$, we shall prove in this section that, if $l(l+1)\hbar^2$ is an eigenvalue of $\mathbf{L}^2$, so is $l(l-1)\hbar^2$. This will obviously exclude the value $l = \frac{1}{2}$, since no eigenvalue of $\mathbf{L}^2$ can be negative. For $(L_\alpha\phi)^*(L_\alpha\phi) = \phi^*L_\alpha^2\phi \geq 0$, for $\alpha = 1$, 2, 3; hence $\phi^*\mathbf{L}^2\phi \geq 0$, and if $\mathbf{L}^2\phi = l(l-1)\hbar^2\phi$, this requires $l(l-1) \geq 0$.

To simplify the proof, we make use of two new results:

RESULT (4): If $L_\sigma = \boldsymbol{\sigma} \cdot \mathbf{L}$, where σ_1, σ_2 and σ_3 are the Pauli matrices defined in 5.3,

$$L_\sigma(L_\sigma+\hbar) = \mathbf{L}^2.$$

PROOF:

$$L_\sigma^2 = \sigma_1^2 L_1^2 + \sigma_2^2 L_2^2 + \sigma_3^2 L_3^2$$
$$+\sigma_1 \sigma_2 L_1 L_2 + \sigma_2 \sigma_1 L_2 L_1$$
$$+\sigma_2 \sigma_3 L_2 L_3 + \sigma_3 \sigma_2 L_3 L_2$$
$$+\sigma_3 \sigma_1 L_3 L_1 + \sigma_1 \sigma_3 L_1 L_3$$
$$= L_1^2 + L_2^2 + L_3^2 + i\sigma_3 (L_1 L_2 - L_2 L_1)$$
$$+i\sigma_1 (L_2 L_3 - L_3 L_2) + i\sigma_2 (L_3 L_1 - L_1 L_3)$$
$$= \mathbf{L}^2 - \hbar(\sigma_3 L_3 + \sigma_1 L_1 + \sigma_2 L_2) \quad.$$

RESULT (5): If $q_\sigma = \boldsymbol{\sigma} \cdot \mathbf{q}$, $L_\sigma q_\sigma + q_\sigma L_\sigma = -2\hbar q_\sigma$.

PROOF:

$$L_\sigma q_\sigma + q_\sigma L_\sigma = 2\sigma_1^2 q_1 L_1 + 2\sigma_2^2 q_2 L_2 + 2\sigma_3^2 q_3 L_3$$
$$+\sigma_1 \sigma_2 (L_1 q_2 + q_1 L_2) + \sigma_2 \sigma_1 (L_2 q_1 + q_2 L_1)$$
$$+\cdots+\cdots$$
$$= 2\mathbf{q} \cdot \mathbf{L} + i\sigma_3 ([L_1,\, q_2] + [q_1,\, L_2]) + \cdots + \cdots$$
$$= 0 - 2\hbar(\sigma_3 q_3 + \sigma_1 q_1 + \sigma_2 q_2).$$

To proceed, let ψ be an eigenvector of $\mathbf{L}^2$, and $l(l+1)\hbar^2$ be the corresponding eigenvalue, so that $\mathbf{L}^2 \psi = l(l+1)\hbar^2 \psi$. Using the result (4), this can be written

$$[L_\sigma(L_\sigma + \hbar) - l(l+1)\hbar^2]\psi = 0$$

or

$$(L_\sigma - l\hbar)(L_\sigma + l\hbar + \hbar)\psi = 0.$$

Thus, if

$$\psi^{(+)} = (L_\sigma + l\hbar + \hbar)\psi,$$
$$\psi^{(-)} = (L_\sigma - l\hbar)\psi,$$

we have $L_\sigma \psi^{(+)} = l\hbar\psi^{(+)}$ and $L_\sigma \psi^{(-)} = -(l+1)\hbar\psi^{(-)}$. So, $\psi^{(+)}$ and $\psi^{(-)}$ are eigenvectors of L_σ, and $l\hbar$ and $-(1+l)\hbar$ are the corresponding eigenvalues.

We now use the result (5) to show that

$$\mathbf{L}^2(q_\sigma \psi^{(-)}) = L_\sigma(L_\sigma + \hbar)q_\sigma \psi^{(-)}$$
$$= -L_\sigma q_\sigma(L_\sigma + \hbar)\psi^{(-)}$$
$$= q_\sigma(L_\sigma + 2\hbar)(L_\sigma + \hbar)\psi^{(-)}$$
$$= l(l-1)\hbar^2(q_\sigma \psi^{(-)}).$$

81

Therefore $\phi = q_\sigma \psi^{(-)}$ is an eigenvector of $\mathbf{L}^2$, and $l(l-1)\hbar^2$ is the corresponding eigenvalue. It follows, in the way already explained, that only integral values are admisible.

Ex. 16: Prove that, if $l(l+1)\hbar^2$ is an eigenvalue of $\mathbf{L}^2$, so is $(l+1)(l+2)\hbar^2$, and deduce that there is no upper limit to l.

5.6 *Eigenvectors and Matrix Elements*

In this section we shall develop a systematic method for constructing the spin matrices of 5.3, and also for representing L_1, L_2 and L_3. For this dual purpose it is convenient again to consider the matrices M_1, M_2 and M_3, concerning which only the relation $\mathbf{M} \wedge \mathbf{M} = i\hbar\mathbf{M}$ is assumed.

Let $\psi^{(j)}$ be a common eigenvector of $\mathbf{M}^2$ and M_3, normalized so that $\psi^{(j)*}\psi^{(j)} = 1$ and satisfying

$$\mathbf{M}^2\psi^{(j)} = m(m+1)\hbar^2\psi^{(j)}, \; M_3\psi^{(j)} = m_3\hbar\psi^{(j)}.$$

We can easily show that if $M_+ = M_1+iM_2$, $M_+\psi^{(j)}$ is also an eigenvector of $\mathbf{M}^2$ and M_3. For $[\mathbf{M}^2, M_+] = 0$, so $\mathbf{M}^2(M_+\psi^{(j)}) = M_+\mathbf{M}^2\psi^{(j)} = m(m+1)\hbar^2 M_+\psi^{(j)}$; and, according to Result (1) of 5.4, $M_3 M_+ = M_+(M_3+\hbar)$, so $M_3(M_+\psi^{(j)}) = M_+(M_3+\hbar)\psi^{(j)} = (m_3+1)\hbar(M_+\psi^{(j)})$. Thus the eigenvalue of $\mathbf{M}^2$ is unchanged, but the eigenvalue of M_3 is increased by $\hbar$, after the application of the operator M_+. But the eigenvector $M_+\psi^{(j)}$ is not yet normalized, and to normalize it we make use again of Result (2) of 5.4, according to which

$$(M_+\psi^{(j)})^*M_+\psi^{(j)} = \psi^{(j)*}M_-M_+\psi^{(j)}$$
$$= \psi^{(j)*}[\mathbf{M}^2 - M_3(M_3+\hbar)]\psi^{(j)}$$
$$= [m(m+1) - m_3(m_3+1)]\hbar^2,$$

since $\psi^{(j)}$ is normalized. Therefore

$$\psi^{(j+1)} = [(m-m_3)(m+m_3+1)\hbar^2]^{-\frac{1}{2}}M_+\psi^{(j)}$$

is the normalized eigenvector. Starting with the vector $\psi^{(1)}$ satisfying $M_3\psi^{(1)} = -m\hbar\psi^{(1)}$, we can use this formula to construct eigenvectors corresponding to the eigenvalues $-(m-1)\hbar$, $-(m-2)\hbar$, ... of M_3. Then $\psi^{(j)}$ will be the eigenvector corresponding to the eigenvalue $(-m+j-1)\hbar$, i.e.,

$$m_3 = -m+j-1.$$

The eigenvectors $\psi^{(j)}$ of M_3 are normal and mutually orthogonal and can be used to construct a representation in which $\mathbf{M}^2$ has the eigenvalue $m(m+1)\hbar^2$, and M_3 is a diagonal matrix. In this representation, $\psi^{(j)} = \delta^{(j)}$ and the matrix elements of M_α are

$$(M_\alpha)_{jk} = \psi^{(j)*}M_\alpha\psi^{(k)} \qquad (j,\ k = 1,\ 2,\ \ldots,\ 2m+1).$$

Since $M_3\psi^{(k)} = (-m+k-1)\hbar\psi^{(k)}$, we have

$$(M_3)_{jk} = \psi^{(j)*}M_3\psi^{(k)} = (-m+k-1)\hbar\delta_{jk}$$

and, since $M_+\psi^{(k)} = [(2m+1-k)k]^{\frac{1}{2}}\hbar\psi^{(k+1)}$,

$$(M_+)_{jk} = \psi^{(j)*}M_+\psi^{(k)} = [(2m+1-k)k]^{\frac{1}{2}}\hbar\delta_{j\,k+1}.$$

Finally, using $(M_-)_{jk} = (M_+)^*_{kj}$, we find

$$(M_-)_{jk} = [(2m+1-j)j]^{\frac{1}{2}}\hbar\delta_{j+1\,k};$$

and since $M_1 = \frac{1}{2}(M_++M_-)$ and $M_2 = \frac{1}{2}i(M_--M_+)$,

$$(M_1)_{jk} = \tfrac{1}{2}[(2m+1-k)k]^{\frac{1}{2}}\hbar\delta_{j\,k+1}+\tfrac{1}{2}[(2m+1-j)j]^{\frac{1}{2}}\hbar\delta_{j+1\,k},$$
$$(M_2)_{jk} = -\tfrac{1}{2}i[2m+1-k)k]^{\frac{1}{2}}\hbar\delta_{j\,k+1}+\tfrac{1}{2}i[(2m+1-j)j]^{\frac{1}{2}}\hbar\delta_{j+1\,k}.$$

The application of these formulae to the spin matrices is direct; for $m = 0, \frac{1}{2}$ and 1, we obtain immediately the representations of S_1, S_2 and S_3 already found in 5.3. If we substitute $m = \frac{3}{2}$ and 2, we obtain in a similar way matrices for higher spin values; it is not, however, certain that particles with these spin values exist in nature.

We can also use the above formulae to obtain a representation of the orbital angular momentum operators, but in this application m is not limited to a single value and takes each of the values $0, 1, 2, \ldots$. If $M_\alpha^{(l)}$ is the matrix corresponding to the value l of m, the matrix representing L_α has the form

$$L_\alpha = \begin{pmatrix} M_\alpha^{(0)} & 0 & 0 & \vdots \\ 0 & M_\alpha^{(1)} & 0 & \vdots \\ 0 & 0 & M_\alpha^{(2)} & \vdots \\ \cdots\cdots\cdots\cdots\cdots\cdots \end{pmatrix},$$

i.e., L_α is the *direct sum* of the matrices $M_\alpha^{(0)}$, $M_\alpha^{(1)}$, $\ldots$. Constructed in this way, L_α will obviously satisfy the relation

$\mathbf{L} \wedge \mathbf{L} = i\hbar\mathbf{L}$, because each of the $M_\alpha{}^{(l)}$ does; also, $\mathbf{L}^2$ will have eigenvalues 0, $2\hbar^2$, $6\hbar^2$, ... equal to the separate eigenvalues of the $\mathbf{M}^{(l)2}$. The number of rows and columns associated with $M_\alpha{}^{(l)}$ is $2l+1$, increasing with l, with the result that the matrices look like this, explicitly:

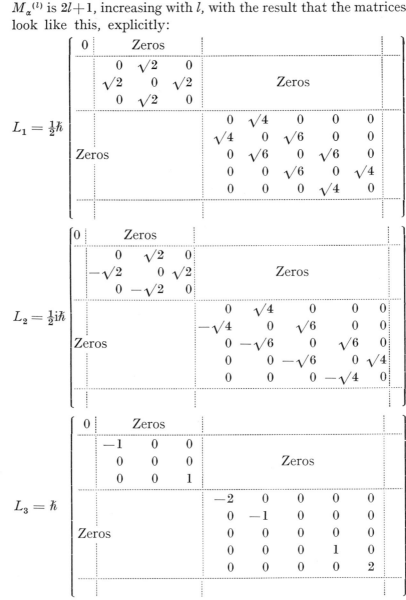

These matrices, of course, extend to infinity.

Ex. 17: From these matrices, obtain the matrix representing $\mathbf{L}^2$ by direct calculation.

EXAMPLES V

1. Starting with the relations

$$L_2L_3-L_3L_2 = i\hbar L_1,$$
$$L_3L_1-L_1L_3 = i\hbar L_2,$$
$$L_1L_2-L_2L_1 = i\hbar L_3,$$

prove that L_3 commutes with $\mathbf{L}^2 = L_1{}^2+L_2{}^2+L_3{}^2$. Writing $L_+ = L_1+iL_2$ and $L_- = L_1-iL_2$, evaluate L_-L_+, L_+L_-, $L_-{}^nL_+{}^n$ and $L_+{}^nL_-{}^n$ in terms of $\mathbf{L}^2$ and L_3.

2. With the notation of 1., suppose $\mathbf{L}^2\psi = l(l+1)\hbar^2\psi$ (where $l \geq 0$) and $L_3\psi = l_3\hbar\psi$. Making use of the fact that $\psi^*L_-{}^nL_+{}^n\psi$ and $\psi^*L_+{}^nL_-{}^n\psi$ must be positive or zero for all values of n, show that (i) $2l$ must be an integer, (ii) $2l_3$ must be an integer between $-2l$ and $2l$, and (iii) $2l-2l_3$ is even.

3. Suppose L_1, L_2 and L_3 are operators satisfying the commutation relations in 1. above, and M_1, M_2 and M_3 are operators satisfying similar commutation relations: $M_2M_3-M_3M_2 = i\hbar$, etc. Suppose also that the L's commute with the M's: $L_\alpha M_\beta = M_\beta L_\alpha$. Prove that if $\mathbf{K} = \mathbf{L}+\mathbf{M}$, then $K_2K_3-K_3K_2 = i\hbar K_1$, etc. Prove that $\mathbf{K}^2$ commutes with $\mathbf{L}^2$, $\mathbf{M}^2$ and $\mathbf{L}\cdot\mathbf{M}$. If $\mathbf{K}^2\psi = k(k+1)\hbar^2\psi$, $\mathbf{L}^2\psi = l(l+1)\hbar^2\psi$ and $\mathbf{M}^2\psi = m(m+1)\hbar^2\psi$, show that

$$\mathbf{L}\cdot\mathbf{M}\psi = \tfrac{1}{2}[k(k+1)-l(l+1)-m(m+1)]\hbar^2\psi.$$

4. With the notation of 3., prove that if $\mathbf{N} = \mathbf{M}^2\mathbf{L}-\mathbf{L}\cdot\mathbf{MM}$, and $\psi^*\psi = 1$,

$$\psi^*\mathbf{N}\cdot\mathbf{N}^*\psi$$
$$= m(m+1)\{l(l+1)m(m+1)-\tfrac{1}{4}[k(k+1)-l(l+1)-m(m+1)]^2\}$$

and hence that (unless $m = 0$)

$$(l+\tfrac{1}{2})(m+\tfrac{1}{2}) > \tfrac{1}{2}[k(k+1)-l(l+1)-m(m+1)].$$

Show that this implies $l+m+1 > k+\frac{1}{2}$, and deduce that $k \leq l+m$. Prove that, if $m = 0$, $k = l$. By similar arguments, show that $l \leq k+m$ and $m \leq k+l$. Is it possible to construct a triangle whose sides have lengths k, l, m, respectively?

5. Let b_r $(r = 1, 2, 3, \ldots)$ be a set of non-hermitean operators satisfying the relations

$$[b_r, [b_s{}^*, b_t]] = \delta_{rs} b_t,$$
$$[b_r, [b_s, b_t]] = 0,$$

where $[A, B]$, as usual, denotes $AB-BA$, and $\delta_{rs} = 0$ unless $r = s$ when $\delta_{ss} = 1$. Show that

$$[b_r{}^*, [b_s, b_t]] = \delta_{rs} b_t - \delta_{rt} b_s,$$
$$[b_r{}^*, [b_s{}^*, b_t{}^*]] = 0,$$

and that $[b_r{}^*, b_r]$ commutes with $[b_s{}^*, b_s]$. Show that all these relations are satisfied if *either* (1) $\{b_r, b_s\} = 0$ and $\{b_r{}^*, b_s\} = \frac{1}{2}\delta_{rs}$, where $\{A, B\}$ means $AB+BA$, or (2) $b_r b_s b_t + b_t b_s b_r = 0$, $b_r{}^* b_s b_t + b_t b_s b_r{}^* = \delta_{rs} b_t$ and $b_r b_s{}^* b_t + b_t b_s{}^* b_r = \delta_{rs} b_t + \delta_{ts} b_r$.

6. Let $L_\sigma = \boldsymbol{\sigma} \cdot \mathbf{L}$, where $\mathbf{L}$ satisfies the relation of 1. above, and $\sigma_1{}^2 = \sigma_2{}^2 = 1$, $\sigma_1 \sigma_2 = -\sigma_2 \sigma_1 = i\sigma_3$. If $L_\sigma \psi = -(l+1)\hbar\psi$, show that $\mathbf{L}^2\psi = l(l+1)\hbar^2\psi$, and hence that $2l$ must be an integer. Let $q_\sigma = \mathbf{q} \cdot \boldsymbol{\sigma}$, and assume that $\mathbf{L} = \mathbf{q} \times \mathbf{p}$; verify that $\mathbf{L}^2(q_\sigma\psi) = (l-1)l\hbar^2(q_\sigma\psi)$.

7. Let P be the *parity operator*, which changes the sign of every co-ordinate and momentum vector and therefore satisfies $P\mathbf{q}+\mathbf{q}P = 0 = P\mathbf{p}+\mathbf{p}P$. Show that P satisfies $P^2 = 1$ and commutes with $\mathbf{L} = \mathbf{q} \times \mathbf{p}$. In the notation of 6., show that, if $P\psi = \psi$, $P(q_\sigma\psi) = -(q_\sigma\psi)$, and deduce that the eigenvalue of P is $\pm(-1)^l$.

8. Show that

$$\exp(iL_3\theta/\hbar)q_1 \exp(-iL_3\theta/\hbar) = q_1 \cos\theta - q_2 \sin\theta,$$
$$\exp(iL_3\theta/\hbar)q_2 \exp(-iL_3\theta/\hbar) = q_2 \cos\theta + q_1 \sin\theta,$$
$$\exp(iL_3\theta/\hbar)q_3 \exp(-iL_3\theta/\hbar) = q_3,$$

and hence that the unitary transformation

$$\mathbf{q} \to \mathbf{q}' = \exp(iL_\alpha\theta/\hbar)\mathbf{q} \exp(-iL_\alpha\theta/\hbar)$$

is equivalent to a rotation of the axes of co-ordinates through an angle θ about the q_α-axis.

9. The spins of the two particles (neutron and proton) forming the deuteron (H^2 nucleus) are $\mathbf{S}^{(1)} = \frac{1}{2}\hbar\boldsymbol{\sigma}^{(1)}$ and $\mathbf{S}^{(2)} = \frac{1}{2}\hbar\boldsymbol{\sigma}^{(2)}$, where $\boldsymbol{\sigma}^{(1)}$ and $\boldsymbol{\sigma}^{(2)}$ are two sets of Pauli matrices which commute with one another $(\sigma_\alpha^{(1)}\sigma_\beta^{(2)} = \sigma_\beta^{(2)}\sigma_\alpha^{(1)})$. If $\sigma_{12} = \boldsymbol{\sigma}^{(1)} \cdot \boldsymbol{\sigma}^{(2)}$, show that $[\frac{1}{2}(1+\sigma_{12})]^2 = 1$, and deduce that an eigenvalue of σ_{12} is either $+1$ or -3. The deuteron is known to have spin 1; its state vector ψ therefore satisfies $(\mathbf{S}^{(1)}+\mathbf{S}^{(2)})^2\psi = 2\hbar^2\psi$. Hence show that $\sigma_{12}\psi = \psi$. Show also, for the state vector ψ' of a neutron and proton with anti-parallel spin, $\sigma_{12}\psi' = -3\psi'$.

10. The spins of the three particles (proton and two neutrons) forming the triton (H^3 nucleus) are $\mathbf{S}^{(1)} = \frac{1}{2}\hbar\boldsymbol{\sigma}^{(1)}$, $\mathbf{S}^{(2)} = \frac{1}{2}\hbar\boldsymbol{\sigma}^{(2)}$ and $\mathbf{S}^{(3)} = \frac{1}{2}\boldsymbol{\sigma}\hbar^{(3)}$. If $\sigma_{ij} = \boldsymbol{\sigma}^{(i)} \cdot \boldsymbol{\sigma}^{(j)}$, prove that

$$(\sigma_{12}+\sigma_{13}+\sigma_{23})^2 = 9,$$

and deduce that the eigenvalue of $\sigma_{12}+\sigma_{13}+\sigma_{23}$ is either -3 or 3. The triton is known to have spin $\frac{1}{2}$; hence show that its state vector satisfies

$$(\sigma_{12}+\sigma_{13}+\sigma_{23})\psi = -3\psi.$$

Prove that σ_{12} commutes with $\sigma_{13}+\sigma_{23}$, and verify the following representation (for the triton)

$$\tfrac{1}{2}(1+\sigma_{12}) = \begin{bmatrix} 1 & 0 \\ 0 & -1 \end{bmatrix},$$

$$\tfrac{1}{2}(1+\sigma_{13}) = \begin{bmatrix} -\frac{1}{2} & -\sqrt{\frac{3}{2}} \\ -\sqrt{\frac{3}{2}} & \frac{1}{2} \end{bmatrix},$$

$$\tfrac{1}{2}(1+\sigma_{23}) = \begin{bmatrix} -\frac{1}{2} & \sqrt{\frac{3}{2}} \\ \sqrt{\frac{3}{2}} & \frac{1}{2} \end{bmatrix}.$$

Optional: Discuss in a similar way the spins of the four particles (two protons and two neutrons) forming the α-particle (He^4 nucleus). The α-particle has spin 0.

6. Further Applications

We shall apply the methods already developed to solve some simple problems in atomic and nuclear phycics.

6.1 *The Energy Levels of the Hydrogen Atom*

Consider a hydrogen atom, or any system consisting of a spherically symmetric positive ion in interaction with an electron (e.g., the He$^+$ ion). Denoting the charges of the positive ion and the electron by Ze and $-e$, respectively, the Coulomb energy of the two particles at distance r is $-Ze^2/r$, in electrostatic units. If the masses and momenta are m_1, $\mathbf{p}_1$ for the electron and m_2, $\mathbf{p}_2$ for the positive ion, the total energy is

$$H = \mathbf{p}_1^2/(2m_1) + \mathbf{p}_2^2/(2m_2) - Ze^2/r.$$

As already explained in 4.5, the kinetic energy can be separated into translational, rotational and vibrational energies, so that the total energy is expressed in the form

$$H = \mathbf{P}^2/(2M) + (p_r^2 + r^{-2}\mathbf{L}^2)/(2m) - Ze^2/r.$$

The translational energy $\mathbf{P}^2/(2M)$ commutes with H; so does $\mathbf{L}^2$ (which commutes with *any* scalar); therefore H, $\mathbf{P}^2/(2M)$, and $\mathbf{L}^2$ have common eigenvectors. If ψ is a common eigenvector, and E, T and $l(l+1)\hbar^2$ are the corresponding eigenvalues, we have

$$H\psi = [T + (p_r^2 + l(l+1)\hbar^2/r^2)/(2m) - Ze^2/r]\psi = E\psi,$$

i.e.,

$$2m(H-T)\psi = [p_r^2 + l(l+1)\hbar^2/r^2 - 2c/r]\psi,$$

where $c = mZe^2$.

So, to determine the energy levels, we have to find the eigenvalues of the linear operator

$$A = p_r^2 + l(l+1)\hbar^2/r^2 - 2c/r.$$

According to the theory of 4.2, the eigenvalues are the set of numbers $a^{(j)}$ defined recursively by

$$A = \theta_1^* \theta_1 + a^{(1)},$$
$$A_{j+1} = \theta_j \theta_j^* + a^{(j)},$$
$$A_j = \theta_j^* \theta_j + a^{(j)},$$

where, in case of ambiguity, the greatest value of $a^{(j)}$ determines the choice of θ_j at each stage.

In this application, the form of A suggests we should take

$$\theta_j = p_r + i(a_j + b_j/r),$$

where a_j and b_j are real numbers, to be determined. Then we shall have

$$\theta_j^* \theta_j = [p_r - i(a_j + b_j/r)][p_r + i(a_j + b_j/r)]$$
$$= p_r^2 + (a_j + b_j/r)^2 + ib_j[p_r, \ r^{-1}]$$
$$= p_r^2 + a_j^2 + 2a_j b_j/r + (b_j^2 - b_j \hbar)/r^2,$$
$$\theta_j \theta_j^* = p_r^2 + (a_j + b_j/r)^2 - ib_j[p_r, \ r^{-1}]$$
$$= p_r^2 + a_j^2 + 2a_j b_j/r + (b_j^2 + b_j \hbar)/r^2.$$

Since (comparing the two expressions for A)

$$\theta_1^* \theta_1 + a^{(1)} = p_r^2 - 2c/r + l(l+1)\hbar^2/r^2,$$

we see that we must choose a_1 and b_1 so that

$$a_1 b_1 = -c, \quad b_1(b_1 - \hbar) = l(l+1)\hbar^2,$$

and $a^{(1)}$ will then be given by

$$a^{(1)} + a_1^2 = 0.$$

There are the possibilities: either (i) $b_1 = -l\hbar$, when $a_1 = c/(l\hbar)$ and $a^{(1)} = -c^2/(l\hbar)^2$, or (ii) $b_1 = (l+1)\hbar$, when $a_1 = -c/[(l+1)\hbar]$ and $a^{(1)} = -c^2/[(l+1)\hbar]^2$. As the second possibility gives the greater value of $a^{(1)}$, this is chosen, i.e., we take $b_1 = (l+1)\hbar$.

Also, since (comparing the two expressions for A_{j+1})

$$\theta_{j+1}^* \theta_{j+1} + a^{(j+1)} = \theta_j \theta_j^* + a^{(j)},$$

we must choose a_{j+1} and b_{j+1} so that

$$a_{j+1}b_{j+1} = a_j b_j, \quad b_{j+1}(b_{j+1}-\hbar) = b_j(b_j+\hbar),$$

and $a^{(j+1)}$ is then given by

$$a^{(j+1)}+a_{j+1} = a^{(j)}+a_j{}^2.$$

There are again two possibilities; either (i) $b_{j+1} = -b_j$ when $a_{j+1} = -a_j$ and $a^{(j+1)} = a^{(j)}$; or (ii) $b_{j+1} = b_j+\hbar = \ldots = b_1+j\hbar = (l+1+j)\hbar,$

$$a_{j+1}b_{j+1} = a_j b_j = \ldots = a_1 b_1 = -c,$$
$$a^{(j+1)}+a_{j+1}^2 = a^{(j)}+a_j{}^2 = \ldots = a^{(1)}+a_1{}^2 = 0,$$

i.e., $b_j = (l+j)\hbar$, $a_j = -c/[(l+j)\hbar]$ and $a^{(j)} = -c^2/[(l+j)\hbar]^2$. The first alternative is obviously unacceptable, so the eigenvalues E of the energy are given by

$$2m(E-T) = -c^2/[(l+j)\hbar]^2,$$

where l is a non-negative integer and j is a positive integer. For a hydrogen atom at rest, $T = 0$ and

$$E = -\frac{mZ^2e^4}{2(l+j)^2\hbar^2}.$$

In addition to these discrete energy levels, there is, according to the theory of 4.2, another possibility: the eigenvalue a may have any value extending from the upper bound (zero) of the $a^{(j)}$. Thus there are also unrestricted positive eigenvalues of the energy. These correspond to states where the electron is not bound, i.e., the hydrogen atom is ionized.

The theory of 4.2 tells us also that the eigenvector $\psi^{(j)}$ must be given by

$$\psi^{(j)} = \theta_1{}^*\theta_2{}^* \ldots \theta^*{}_{j-1}\phi^{(j-1)}$$

(or $\phi^{(0)}$ for $j = 1$), where $\theta_j \phi^{(j-1)} = 0$, i.e.,

$$[p_r+i(a_j+b_j/r)]\phi^{(j-1)} = 0.$$

This enables the eigenvectors to be constructed in the way suggested by the following example.

Ex. 18: If χ is the eigenvector of p_r corresponding to the eigenvalue zero, i.e., $p_r\chi = 0$, show that $\phi^{(j-1)} = r^{l+j} \exp(a_j r/\hbar)\chi$.

6.2 *The Deuteron*

The deuteron is a bound state of a proton and neutron. As the neutron is uncharged, there are no electrostatic forces involved, and one is concerned with only the short range nuclear forces. Owing to complexities arising from the spin of the two particles, pair production within the nucleus, etc., the nuclear forces are quite complicated in detail, but to a good approximation the interaction energy of the proton and neutron is represented by Hulthen's potential

$$V(r) = -\frac{g\mu^2}{e^{\mu r}-1},$$

where g is a known constant and μ is the mass of the π-meson, multiplied by $c/\hbar$, where c is the velocity of light. From the small electrical quadrupole moment of the deuteron it is inferred that the eigenvalue zero of L^2 predominates, though there is a small probability of the eigenvalue $6\hbar^2$ which will be neglected here. The energy of a deuteron at rest may therefore be assumed to be

$$H = p_r^2/(2m) + V(r),$$

where m, the reduced mass, is about *one half* the proton mass. So we have to investigate the eigenvalues of

$$A = p_r^2 - c\mu^2/(e^{\mu r}-1),$$

where $c = 2mg$.

This time we take

$$\theta_j = p_r + ia_j + ib_j/(e^{\mu r}-1)$$

and find

$$\begin{aligned}
\theta_j^*\theta_j &= p_r^2 + [a_j + b_j/(e^{\mu r}-1)]^2 + ib_j[p_r,\ (e^{\mu r}-1)^{-1}]\\
&= p_r^2 + a_j^2 + 2a_j b_j/(e^{\mu r}-1) + b_j^2/(e^{\mu r}-1)^2\\
&\quad -b_j\hbar\mu\ e^{\mu r}/(e^{\mu r}-1)^2\\
&= p_r^2 + a_j^2 + (2a_j - \hbar\mu)b_j/(e^{\mu r}-1)\\
&\quad + b_j(b_j - \hbar\mu)/(e^{\mu r}-1)^2.
\end{aligned}$$

Similarly,

$$\begin{aligned}
\theta_j\theta_j^* &= p_r^2 + a_j^2 + (2a_j + \hbar\mu)b_j/(e^{\mu r}-1)\\
&\quad + b_j(b_j + \hbar\mu)/(e^{\mu r}-1)^2.
\end{aligned}$$

Since $A = \theta_1*\theta_1 + a^{(1)}$, we find (rejecting $b_1 = 0$) $b_1 = \hbar\mu$, $(2a_1 - \hbar\mu)b_1 = -2c$, and $a^{(1)} + a_1{}^2 = 0$. Thus $a_1 = \frac{1}{2}\hbar\mu - c/(\hbar\mu)$ and $a^{(1)} = -[c/(\hbar\mu) - \frac{1}{2}\hbar\mu]^2$. This is the negative binding energy of the deuteron.

Ex. 19: Find $a^{(2)}$, and hence the condition which c must satisfy for the existence of a second bound level of the deuteron. (This condition is actually not satisfied: there is only one bound level. However, excited levels have some interest in the theory of neutron-proton scattering).

6.3 Particle in a Box

Consider a particle confined within a rectangular box, so that the eigenvalues λ_q of any co-ordinate q all lie in the interval $-\frac{1}{2}l < \lambda_q < \frac{1}{2}l$, where l is the length of the box in a particular direction. The energy associated with the motion in this direction is simply

$$H = p^2/2m.$$

(The total energy will be a sum of three terms of this type, which commute with one another and therefore have common eigenvectors). To find the eigenvalues of $A = 2mH = p^2$, we try

$$\theta_j = p + ia_j \tan (b_j q),$$

noticing that, since the tangent does not exist for the arguments $-\pi/2$ and $\pi/2$, the greatest eigenvalues of $b_j q$, namely $\pm\frac{1}{2}b_j l$, must not exceed these values, i.e., $|b_j| \leq \pi/l$. We find

$$\theta_j*\theta_j = p^2 + a_j{}^2 \tan^2 (b_j q) + ia_j[p, \ \tan (b_j q)]$$
$$= p^2 + a_j{}^2 \tan^2 (b_j q) + a_j b_j \hbar \sec^2 (b_j q)$$
$$= p^2 + a_j b_j \hbar + a_j(a_j + b_j \hbar) \tan^2 (b_j q)$$

and

$$\theta_j \theta_j* = p^2 - a_j b_j \hbar + a_j(a_j - b_j \hbar) \tan^2 (b_j q).$$

Since

$$\theta_1*\theta_1 + a^{(1)} = p^2,$$

we must take $a_1(a_1 + b_1 \hbar) = 0$, i.e., (rejecting $a_1 = 0$) $a_1 = -b_1 \hbar$; also $a_1 b_1 \hbar + a^{(1)} = 0$, so $a^{(1)} = a_1{}^2 = (b_1 \hbar)^2$. The maximum value of $a^{(1)}$ is obtained by giving b_1 its maximum value which, as already noticed, is π/l. Hence $a^{(1)} = (\pi\hbar/l)^2$.

Next we use

$$\theta_{j+1}^* \theta_{j+1} + a^{(j+1)} = \theta_j \theta_j^* + a^{(j)},$$

which requires us to take $b_{j+1} = b_j$ and $a_{j+1}(a_{j+1}+b_{j+1}\hbar) = a_j(a_j-b_j\hbar)$, and shows that the eigenvalues satisfy

$$a^{(j+1)} + a_{j+1}b_{j+1}\hbar = a^{(j)} - a_j b_j \hbar,$$

i.e.,

$$a^{(j+1)} - a_{j+1}^2 = a^{(j)} - a_j^2 = \ldots = a^{(1)} - a_1^2 = 0.$$

So $a^{(j)} = a_j^2$, where, since $b_{j+1} = b_j = \ldots = b_1 = \pi/l$,

$$a_{j+1}(a_{j+1}+\pi\hbar/l) = a_j(a_j-\pi\hbar/l).$$

Rejecting the solution $a_{j+1} = -a_j$, this gives us

$$a_{j+1} = a_j - \pi\hbar/l = \ldots = a_1 - j\pi\hbar/l = -(j+1)\pi\hbar/l.$$

So $a_j = -j\pi\hbar/l$ and

$$a^{(j)} = (j\pi\hbar/l)^2.$$

The eigenvalues of the energy H are therefore $(j\pi\hbar/l)^2/(2m)$, where j is a positive integer. For a box with sides l_1, l_2 and l_3, the eigenvalues of the total energy are

$$(j_1^2/l_1^2 + j_2^2/l_2^2 + j_3^2/l_3^2)(\pi\hbar)^2/(2m),$$

where j_1, j_2 and j_3 are positive integers.

Ex. 20: If $\theta_1\phi^{(0)} = 0$ and $\phi^{(j)} = \cos^j(b_1 q)\phi^{(0)}$, prove that $\theta_j\phi^{(j-1)} = 0$, and hence express the eigenvector $\psi^{(j)}$ corresponding to the eigenvalue $a^{(j)}$ in terms of $\psi^{(1)}$.

6.4 *Perturbation Theory*

Only the simplest problems of matrix mechanics are exactly soluble, and very often approximate methods have to be used. One of the most useful methods is that provided by perturbation theory. The idea is as follows.

Suppose it is not possible to find the eigenvalues and eigenvectors of H exactly, but $H = H_0 + \alpha V$, where the eigenvalues and eigenvectors of H_0 are known, and α is a numerical parameter which can be regarded as small. Then the eigenvalue equation

$$H\psi^{(j)} = (H_0 + \alpha V)\psi^{(j)} = E^{(j)}\psi^{(j)} \qquad (6.1)$$

can be solved by expanding $\psi^{(j)}$ and $E^{(j)}$ in powers of α, thus:

$$\psi^{(j)} = \psi_0^{(j)} + \alpha\psi_1^{(j)} + \alpha^2\psi_2^{(j)} + \ldots,$$
$$E^{(j)} = E_0^{(j)} + \alpha E_1^{(j)} + \alpha^2 E_2^{(j)} + \ldots.$$

Substituting these expressions in (6.1), we have

$$(H_0 + \alpha V - E_0^{(j)} - \alpha E_1^{(j)} - \alpha^2 E_2^{(j)} - \ldots)$$
$$\times (\psi_0^{(j)} + \alpha\psi_1^{(j)} + \alpha^2\psi_2^{(j)} + \ldots) = 0.$$

As this is true for all values of α, we can equate the coefficients of the various powers of α to zero, and obtain

$$(H_0 - E_0^{(j)})\psi_0^{(j)} = 0,$$
$$(H_0 - E_0^{(j)})\psi_1^{(j)} + (V - E_1^{(j)})\psi_0^{(j)} = 0,$$
$$(H_0 - E_0^{(j)})\psi_2^{(j)} + (V - E_1^{(j)})\psi_1^{(j)} - E_2^{(j)}\psi_0^{(j)} = 0, \qquad (6.2)$$

etc. The first equation tells us that $E_0^{(j)}$ is one of the *known* eigenvalues of H_0, and $\psi_0^{(j)}$ the corresponding eigenvector, also known. From the second equation we can determine $E_1^{(j)}$ and $\psi_1^{(j)}$. For, multiplying by $\psi_0^{(j)*}$ and using

$$\psi_0^{(j)*}H_0\psi_1^{(j)} = (H_0\psi_0^{(j)})^*\psi_1^{(j)} = E_0^{(j)}\psi_0^{(j)*}\psi_1^{(j)},$$

we obtain $\psi_0^{(j)*}(V - E_1^{(j)})\psi_0^{(j)} = 0$, i.e.,

$$E_1^{(j)} = \psi_0^{(j)*}V\psi_0^{(j)},$$

assuming that $\psi_0^{(j)}$ is normalized. Also, multiplying by $\psi_0^{(k)*}$, where $k \neq j$ and hence $\psi_0^{(k)*}\psi_0^{(j)} = 0$, we have

$$(E_0^{(k)} - E_0^{(j)})\psi_0^{(k)*}\psi_1^{(j)} + \psi_0^{(k)*}V\psi_0^{(j)} = 0,$$

i.e.,

$$\psi_0^{(k)*}\psi_1^{(j)} = (E_0^{(j)} - E_0^{(k)})^{-1}\psi_0^{(k)*}V\psi_0^{(j)}.$$

Hence

$$\psi_1^{(j)} = \Sigma_k(\psi_0^{(k)*}\psi_1^{(j)})\psi_0^{(k)}$$
$$= \Sigma_k(E_0^{(j)} - E_0^{(k)})^{-1}(\psi_0^{(k)*}V\psi_0^{(j)})\psi_0^{(k)}.$$

The third equation (6.2) can be used to determine $E_2^{(j)}$ and $\psi_2^{(j)}$ in a similar way, and so on. But if the potential αV is really small compared with H_0, the energy levels are $E_0^{(j)} + \alpha E_1^{(j)}$, to a good approximation, and $\psi_0^{(j)}+\alpha\psi_1^{(j)}$ is, very nearly, the corresponding eigenvector.

This method has many applications. For instance, it can be used to determine the effect of the term $(1/6)V''(a)(r-a\,\mathbf{1})^3$ neglected from the energy in **3.4** (i). Another very important application is to scattering problems. Here H_0 will usually be the sum of the kinetic energies of two weakly interacting particles, and αV their interaction energy; $\psi_0^{(j)}$ will be the vector representing the state of the particles in the absence of scattering, and $\alpha\psi_1^{(j)}$ will represent approximately the state of the particles when scattering has taken place. In this application, one is frequently interested in what is called the S-matrix, which is the matrix $\psi_0^{(k)*}S\psi_0^{(j)}$ representing the operator defined by $\psi^{(j)} = S\psi_0^{(j)}$. According to the above calculation, one has

$$\psi_0^{(k)*}S\psi_0^{(j)} = \psi_0^{(k)*}\psi^{(j)} = \delta_{jk}+\alpha\psi_0^{(k)*}\psi_1^{(j)}$$
$$= \delta_{jk}+\alpha(E_0^{(j)}-E_0^{(k)})^{-1}\psi_0^{(k)*}V\psi_0^{(j)}$$

approximately.

6.5 *Continuous Representations*

The applications considered in this book have all been effected with vectors possessing at most a countably infinite set of components. While there are no problems which cannot be treated in this way, it is often convenient to make use of representations in which the vectors have an uncountable number of components and ψ_k is to be regarded as a function $\Psi(k)$ of a continuous variable k. The operators applied to such vectors are frequently integral or differential operators. An important special case occurs where the vector components are eigenvectors of the co-ordinate variables, which all commute and therefore possess common eigenvalues. Then one will be able to regard the co-ordinates q_α as numbers, rather than operators. The commutation relations

$$q_\alpha p_\beta - p_\beta q_\alpha = i\hbar\delta_{\alpha\beta}$$

are then satisfied, provided p_β is the differential operator

$$p_\beta = -i\hbar\frac{\partial}{\partial q_\beta}.$$

This representation is used in wave mechanics, together with the time-dependent canonical transformation described in 4.1. There are, however, other continuous representations; one, which is frequently used, makes the vector components eigenvectors of the momenta. In this representation, the p_β may be regarded as numbers, and the co-ordinates are represented as differential operators:

$$q_\alpha = i\hbar \frac{\partial}{\partial p_\alpha}.$$

In this book, nearly all the mathematical work is quite independent of the particular representation in mind, and is equally valid when the operators are matrix, integral or differential operators. The student familiar with wave mechanics will find it instructive to substitute differential operators for the momenta wherever they have appeared and compare the development with that which is more often used in elementary wave mechanics.

EXAMPLES VI

1. If $A = p^2 - 2\hbar k q^{-1} + l(l+1)\hbar^2 q^{-2}$ and $qp - pq = i\hbar$, show that

$$A = \theta_1^* \theta_1 - k^2/(l+1)^2,$$

where $\theta_1 = p + i\hbar(l+1)q^{-1} - ik/(l+1)$. Deduce that the least eigenvalue of A, when $k > 0$, is $-k^2/(l+1)^2$; and determine the other eigenvalues. By substituting $\hbar k = mZe^2$, obtain the energy levels of the hydrogen atom.

2. A particle of mass m is known to be within a large sphere of radius R, centred at the origin of co-ordinates. Express the energy of the particle in the form

$$H = (p_r^2 + \mathbf{L}^2/r^2)/(2m),$$

where $rp_r - p_r r = i\hbar$. Suppose ψ_l is an eigenvector of both H and $\mathbf{L}^2$, corresponding to the eigenvalue $l(l+1)\hbar^2$ of $\mathbf{L}^2$, so that if λ_l is the eigenvalue of $2mH$,

$$[p_r^2 + l(l+1)\hbar^2/r^2]\psi_l = \lambda_l \psi_l.$$

Consider first the possibility $l = 0$. Using the fact that r has eigenvalue between 0 and R, show that the appropriate form of θ_j is

$$\theta_j = p_r + (ij\pi\hbar/R) \cot (\pi r/R)$$

and that the j-th eigenvalue is

$$\lambda_0^{(j)} = (j\pi\hbar/R)^2 \qquad (j = 1,\ 2,\ 3,\ \ldots).$$

3. With the same notation as used in 2. above, obtain the lowest eigenvalue for general values of l, in the following way. Let $\alpha_j = p_r + ij\hbar/r$ and show that the eigenvalue problem reduces to solving

$$\alpha_l \alpha_l^* \psi_l = \lambda_l \psi_l.$$

Prove that $\alpha_1^* \alpha_1 = p_r^2$ and $\alpha_{j+1}^* \alpha_{j+1} = \alpha_j \alpha_j^*$.

Hence show that the eigenvector corresponding to the least eigenvalue $\lambda_l^{(1)}$ is

$$\psi_l^{(1)} = \alpha_l \alpha_{l-1} \cdots \alpha_1 \phi_l,$$

if ϕ_l satisfies

$$[p_r + ic_l \hbar \cot (c_l r)]\phi_l = 0$$

and $c_l^2 = \lambda_l^{(1)}$. Prove that

$$\psi_1^{(1)} = i\hbar[r^{-1} - c_1 \cot (c_1 r)]\phi_1,$$

$$\psi_2^{(1)} = (i\hbar)^2[3r^{-2} - 3c_2 r^{-1} \cot (c_2 r) - c_2^2]\phi_2,$$

and, in general,

$$\psi_l^{(1)} = (i\hbar c_l)^l g_l(c_l r)\phi_l,$$

where

$$g_{l+1}(x) = (l+1)g_l(x)/x - g_l(x) \cot x - g'_l(x).$$

Deduce that c_l should be chosen so that

$$\cot (c_l b) + g'_l(c_l b)/g_l(c_l b)$$

varies between $-\infty$ and $+\infty$ in the range $0 < b < R$, and hence that $c_l R$ is the smallest positive root of the transcendental equation $g_l(c_l R) = 0$.

4. Prove with the notation of 2. and 3. that $\lambda_l^{(2)} = c_l^2$, where c_l is the second smallest positive root of the equation $g_l(c_l R) = 0$; generalize this result to determine $\lambda_l^{(j)}$.

5. Consider a particle of mass m, in a field of potential energy $V(r)$, so that the eigenvalue problem to be solved reduces to

$$[p_r^2+l(l+1)\hbar^2/r^2+2mV(r)]\psi_l = \lambda_l\psi_l,$$

where λ_l is the eigenvalue of $2mH$. Assume that the particle is in a sphere of radius R, and show that for $l = 0$ the appropriate form of θ_j is

$$\theta_j = p_r+if_j(r),$$

where

$$2mV(r)=[f_1(r)]^2+\hbar f'_1(r)+\lambda_0^{(1)}$$

and

$$[f_{j+1}(r)]^2+\hbar f'_{j-1}(r)+\lambda_0^{(j+1)} = [f_j(r)]^2-\hbar f'_j(r)+\lambda_0^{(j)}.$$

6. With the notation of 5., consider the 'square well' potential defined by

$$V(b) = -V \text{ for } b < a$$
$$= 0 \text{ for } b > a.$$

Show that, for $b \leq a$, $f_1(b) = c_1\hbar \cot (c_1 b)$, and that $\lambda_0^{(1)} = c_1^2\hbar^2-2mV$. If $\lambda_0^{(1)} > 0$, so that there are no bound states, show that for $b \geq a$, $f_1(b) = c'_1\hbar \cot (c'_1 b+\eta_1)$ and $\lambda_0^{(1)} = c'_1^2\hbar^2$, where $c'_1 R+\eta_1 = \pi$. Deduce that the *phase shift* η_1 is obtained by elimination from the equations

$$c_1\hbar \cot (c_1 a) = c'_1\hbar \cot (c'_1 a+\eta_1),$$
$$c_1^2\hbar^2-2mV = c'_1^2\hbar^2,$$
$$c'_1 R+\eta_1 = \pi,$$

when the energy of the particle is $c'_1^2\hbar^2/(2m)$.

7. With the notation of 6., show that when $\lambda_0^{(1)} < 0$,

$$f_1(b)=(-\lambda_0^{(1)})^{\frac{1}{2}} \text{ for } b \geq a,$$

and the value of c_1 is given by the equation

$$\sin (c_1 a) = \hbar c_1/(2mV)^{\frac{1}{2}}.$$

Determine the energy of the bound state.

8. Generalize the analysis of 6. to show that, when there is no bound state,

$$f_j(b) = jc_j\hbar \cot (c_jb) \text{ for } b \le a,$$
$$f_j(b) = jc'_j\hbar \cot (c'_jb+\eta_j) \text{ for } b \ge a;$$

and

$$\lambda_0{}^{(j)} = j^2c_j{}^2\hbar^2-V = j^2c'_j{}^2\hbar^2.$$

Hence show that the constants c_j, c'_j and η_j are given by

$$c_j \cot (c_ja) = c'_j \cot (c'_ja+\eta_j),$$
$$c_j{}^2\hbar^2-V/j^2 = c'_j{}^2\hbar^2,$$
$$c'_j R+\eta_j = \pi.$$

9. Suppose, in the context of 6., that there is a second bound state. Find the minimum value of V for which this can occur, and determine $\lambda_0{}^{(2)}$.

10. Re-examine the analysis of 5., 6., 7., 8. and 9. for $l = 1$.

7. Relativistic Quantum Mechanics

Newtonian mechanics, and also ordinary quantum mechanics, are based on principles which include two kinematical postulates. They assume

(1) that the time between two events is a physical quantity which has a definite value, in given units, independent of the observer,

(2) that the distance between two simultaneous events is a physical quantity which has a definite value, in given units, independent of the observer.

The notion of absolute simultaneity depends on the concept of absolute time, and therefore the second postulate presupposes the first. These postulates establish a relation between the descriptions of events given by observers in relative motion. If $\mathbf{x}$ is the vector separation of two events E_1 and E_2, and t the time between these events, found by an observer O, and $\mathbf{x}'$, t' are the corresponding quantities found by an observer O', moving with velocity $\mathbf{v}$ relative to O, it can be inferred from (1) and (2) that

$$t' = t, \qquad \mathbf{x}' = \mathbf{x} - \mathbf{v}t,$$

provided O and O' choose coordinate axes which are parallel to one another. Thus, if $\mathbf{u} = \mathbf{x}/t$ is the mean velocity of any signal transmitted between the events E_1 and E_2, measured by O, the mean velocity measured by O' will be $\mathbf{u}' = \mathbf{x}'/t' = \mathbf{u} - \mathbf{v}$. Experimentally, the speed of a light signal is found to be independent of the state of motion of the observer; thus if, $|\mathbf{u}| = c$, we should have $|\mathbf{u} - \mathbf{v}| = c$, whatever the value of $\mathbf{v}$. But, as this is just not true, the postulates (1) and (2) must be rejected in relativistic theory. They are replaced by an intrinsically simpler postulate:

(3) the *intervals* between two events, defined as $s = (t^2 - \mathbf{x}^2/c^2)^{\frac{1}{2}}$

in the notation already explained, is a physical quantity which has the same definite value, in given units, for all force-free observers.

It is an immediate consequence of this postulate that if O and O' are force-free observers, and a signal is transmitted with the velocity c between the two events E_1 and E_2, so that $|\mathbf{x}|/t = c$ for O, then $s' = s = 0$ and $|\mathbf{x}'|/t' = c$ for O 'also. Thus, on empirical grounds, c may be identified with the velocity of light. The postulate (3) leads to the relations (known as the Lorentz transformation)

$$t' = \gamma(t - \mathbf{v} \cdot \mathbf{x}/c^2), \qquad \gamma = (1 - \mathbf{v}^2/c^2)^{-\frac{1}{2}},$$
$$\mathbf{v} \cdot \mathbf{x}' = \gamma(\mathbf{v} \cdot \mathbf{x} - \mathbf{v}^2 t), \qquad \mathbf{v} \wedge \mathbf{x}' = \mathbf{v} \wedge \mathbf{x},$$

connecting the vector separation $\mathbf{x}$ and time difference t between two events, found by O, and the corresponding quantities $\mathbf{x}'$ and t' found by O'. These relations assume O' has chosen coordinate axes parallel to those of O.

The important application of these results, from our point of view, is that if $\mathbf{dq}$ is the displacement of a particle in the time dt, measured by the observer O, the interval

$$ds = (dt^2 - \mathbf{dq}^2/c^2)^{\frac{1}{2}}$$
$$= (1 - \dot{\mathbf{q}}^2/c^2)^{\frac{1}{2}} dt$$

is an invariant, i.e., has the same value, in the same units, for any other force-free observer O'; and

$$dt' = \gamma(dt - \mathbf{v} \cdot \mathbf{dq}/c^2),$$
$$\mathbf{v} \cdot \mathbf{dq}' = \gamma(\mathbf{v} \cdot \mathbf{dq} - v^2 dt), \qquad \mathbf{v} \wedge \mathbf{dq}' = \mathbf{v} \wedge \mathbf{dq}.$$

A further difference between classical and relativistic mechanics affects the form of the Lagrangian function L, which has to be carefully chosen so the equations of motion will take the same form for all force-free observers. This requires that the action

$$A = \int_{t_0}^{t} L \, dt$$

should be independent of the state of motion of the observer.

For a single particle, in the absence of impressed forces, this will obviously be so if

$$L = -mc^2 \, ds/dt$$
$$= -mc^2(1-\dot{\mathbf{q}}^2/c^2)^{\frac{1}{2}},$$

where m is the mass of the particle. Although this looks quite different from the non-relativistic Lagrangian $L_n = \frac{1}{2}m\dot{\mathbf{q}}^2$ for a free particle, it is easy to see that, when $\dot{\mathbf{q}}^2/c^2$ is small, the difference $L_n - L \approx mc^2$, which is a constant and will not appear in the equation of motion of the particle.

The only forces we shall need to consider will be electro-magnetic forces. We assume that Maxwell's equations, which include

$$\nabla \wedge \mathbf{E} = -\dot{\mathbf{B}}/c, \quad \nabla \cdot \mathbf{B} = 0, \quad (\nabla = \partial/\partial\mathbf{x})$$

where $\mathbf{E}$ is the electric intensity and $\mathbf{B}$ the magnetic induction, are unchanged. They can, therefore, be satisfied in the usual way by writing

$$\mathbf{E} = -\nabla\phi - \dot{\mathbf{A}}/c, \qquad \mathbf{B} = \nabla \wedge \mathbf{A},$$

where ϕ is the scalar potential and $\mathbf{A}$ is the vector potential of the field. These potentials are not completely determined unless some additional condition is imposed on them; the *Lorentz condition*

$$\nabla \cdot \mathbf{A} = -\dot{\phi}/c$$

is the most convenient for relativistic calculations.

We adopt, as the relativistic Lagrangian function of a particle of charge e in an electromagnetic field,

$$L = -mc^2(1-\dot{\mathbf{q}}^2/c^2)^{\frac{1}{2}} - e\phi(\mathbf{q}) + e\dot{\mathbf{q}} \cdot \mathbf{A}(\mathbf{q})/c,$$

where $\phi(\mathbf{q})$ and $\mathbf{A}(\mathbf{q})$ are the values of the potentials ϕ and $\mathbf{A}$ at the point $\mathbf{q}$ where the particle is situated. This differs from the corresponding non-relativistic Lagrangian only through the appearance of $-mc^2(1-\dot{\mathbf{q}}^2/c^2)$ instead of $\frac{1}{2}m\dot{\mathbf{q}}^2$. The momentum of the particle, obtained in the usual way by differentiating L with respect to $\dot{\mathbf{q}}$, is

$$\mathbf{p} = m\dot{\mathbf{q}}(1-\dot{\mathbf{q}}/c^2)^{-\frac{1}{2}} + e\mathbf{A}(\mathbf{q})/c;$$

and the equations of motion of the particle are

$$\frac{d\mathbf{p}}{dt} = \frac{\partial L}{\partial \mathbf{q}} = -e\frac{\partial}{\partial \mathbf{q}}\,[\phi(\mathbf{q}) - \dot{\mathbf{q}}\cdot\mathbf{A}(\mathbf{q})/c].$$

Since

$$\frac{d\mathbf{A}(\mathbf{q})}{dt} = \dot{\mathbf{A}}(\mathbf{q}) + \dot{\mathbf{q}}\cdot\frac{\partial}{\partial \mathbf{q}}\,\mathbf{A}(\mathbf{q})$$

and

$$\frac{\partial}{\partial \mathbf{q}}\,[\dot{\mathbf{q}}\cdot\mathbf{A}(\mathbf{q})] - \dot{\mathbf{q}}\cdot\frac{\partial}{\partial \mathbf{q}}\,\mathbf{A}(\mathbf{q}) = \dot{\mathbf{q}}\wedge\mathbf{B}(\mathbf{q})$$

(because $\mathbf{B} = \nabla\wedge\mathbf{A}$), the equation of motion can be rewritten

$$\frac{d}{dt}\left[\frac{m\dot{\mathbf{q}}}{(1-\dot{\mathbf{q}}^2/c^2)^{\frac{1}{2}}}\right] = e[\mathbf{E}(\mathbf{q}) + \dot{\mathbf{q}}\wedge\mathbf{B}(\mathbf{q})/c].$$

Finally, the energy of the particle is

$$H = \dot{\mathbf{q}}\cdot\mathbf{p} - L$$
$$= mc^2(1-\dot{\mathbf{q}}^2/c^2)^{-\frac{1}{2}} + e\phi(\mathbf{q}).$$

When $\dot{\mathbf{q}}^2/c^2$ is small, the approximation $(1-\dot{\mathbf{q}}^2/c^2)^{-\frac{1}{2}} \approx 1+\frac{1}{2}\dot{\mathbf{q}}^2/c^2$ is valid, and $H \approx mc^2 + \frac{1}{2}m\dot{\mathbf{q}}^2 + e\phi(\mathbf{q})$. This differs from the non-relativistic Hamiltonian $H_n = \frac{1}{2}m\dot{\mathbf{q}}^2 + e\phi(\mathbf{q})$ only by mc^2. The energy may also be expressed in Hamiltonian form, by eliminating $\dot{\mathbf{q}}$ in favour of the momentum $\mathbf{p}$:

$$H = c\{m^2c^2 + [\mathbf{p} - e\mathbf{A}(\mathbf{q})/c]^2\}^{\frac{1}{2}} + e\phi(\mathbf{q}).$$

In the above sketch of the classical relativistic mechanics of a particle, $\mathbf{q}$, $\dot{\mathbf{q}}$ and $\mathbf{p}$ are of course to be regarded as ordinary variables, taking numerical values, and not as operators. In the remainder of this section we shall examine the quantum-mechanical generalization.

7.1 *The Transition to Quantum Mechanics*

In relativistic quantum mechanics, the formula

$$\mathbf{p} = m\dot{\mathbf{q}}(1-\dot{\mathbf{q}}/c^2)^{-\frac{1}{2}} + e\mathbf{A}(\mathbf{q})/c$$

for the momentum, and the expression

$$H = c\{m^2c^2 + [\mathbf{p} - e\mathbf{A}(\mathbf{q})/c]^2\}^{\frac{1}{2}} + e\phi(\mathbf{q})$$

103

for the energy are taken unchanged from the classical theory; but $\mathbf{q}$, $\dot{\mathbf{q}}$ and $\mathbf{p}$ are operators which do not commute. The commutation relation

$$LH - HL = i\hbar\frac{dL}{dt}$$

of non-relativistic theory is not altered, and, in particular, the relation

$$\mathbf{q}H - H\mathbf{q} = i\hbar\dot{\mathbf{q}}$$

must be satisfied. This relation will in fact be satisfied if

$$q_\alpha p_\beta - p_\beta q_\alpha = i\hbar\delta_{\alpha\beta},$$

for then

$$\mathbf{q}H - H\mathbf{q} = i\hbar\frac{\partial H(\mathbf{q};\ \mathbf{p})}{\partial \mathbf{p}}$$

$$= i\hbar c[\mathbf{p} - e\mathbf{A}(\mathbf{q})/c]\{m^2c^2 + [\mathbf{p} - e\mathbf{A}(\mathbf{q})/c]^2\}^{-\frac{1}{2}}$$

and, if we eliminate $\mathbf{p}$, the right side of this equation reduces to $i\hbar\dot{\mathbf{q}}$. Also, we must have

$$i\hbar\dot{\mathbf{p}} = \mathbf{p}H - H\mathbf{p},$$

and this leads to

$$\frac{d\mathbf{p}}{dt} = -\frac{\partial H(\mathbf{q};\ \mathbf{p})}{\partial \mathbf{q}},$$

which is simply the classical equation of motion in operational form.

If our object in quantum mechanics were simply to determine the operators $\mathbf{q}$ and $\mathbf{p}$ at time t, given their 'values' $\mathbf{q}_0$ and $\mathbf{p}_0$ at time t_0, we could write down the results at once:

$$\mathbf{q} = \exp[iH(t-t_0)/\hbar]\mathbf{q}_0\exp[-iH(t-t_0)/\hbar],$$
$$\mathbf{p} = \exp[iH(t-t_0)/\hbar]\mathbf{p}_0\exp[-iH(t-t_0)/\hbar].$$

However, the actual problems which we wish to solve are not the same as in classical mechanics. In fact, our main interest will ultimately be in the determination of the eigenvalues and eigenvectors of the energy.

7.2 *Particles and Anti-Particles*

Consider first a neutral particle, or a charged particle with no electromagnetic field. Then

$$H = c(m^2c^2 + \mathbf{p}^2)^{\frac{1}{2}}.$$

The square root which appears in the relativistic Hamiltonian is ambiguous: there is, of course, not just one square root of an operator, or even two, as for a number. In making clear just which square root is implied we shall discover possibilities with important physical consequences.

Let ψ be an eigenvector of H, and let E be the corresponding eigenvalue, so that

$$H\psi = E\psi.$$

Then $c^2(m^2c^2 + \mathbf{p}^2)\psi = H^2\psi = HE\psi = E^2\psi$, i.e.,

$$(E^2/c^2 - m^2c^2)\psi = \mathbf{p}^2\psi.$$

Now, it has been shown in 6.3 that, if the particle is within a rectangular region with sides of length l_1, l_2 and l_3, the eigenvalues of p_1, p_2 and p_3 are

$$k_1 = j_1\pi\hbar/l_1, \quad k_2 = j_2\pi\hbar/l_2, \quad k_3 = j_3\pi\hbar/l_3,$$

respectively, where j_1, j_2 and j_3 are integers. Therefore

$$E^2/c^2 - m^2c^2 = \mathbf{k}^2,$$

$$\mathbf{k}^2 = k_1^2 + k_2^2 + k_3^2 = (j_1^2/l_1^2 + j_2^2/l_2^2 + j_3^2/l_3^2)\pi^2\hbar^2$$

and

$$E = \pm c(m^2c^2 + \mathbf{k}^2)^{\frac{1}{2}}.$$

Let ψ_+ and ψ_- be the eigenvector corresponding to the eigenvalues $+c(m^2c^2 + \mathbf{k}^2)^{\frac{1}{2}}$ and $-c(m^2c^2 + \mathbf{k}^2)^{\frac{1}{2}}$, respectively, so that

$$H\psi_+ = c(m^2c^2 + \mathbf{k}^2)^{\frac{1}{2}}\psi_+,$$

$$H\psi_- = -c(m^2c^2 + \mathbf{k}^2)^{\frac{1}{2}}\psi_-.$$

The last equation might be interpreted as meaning that the measured value of the energy, in the state associated with the eigenvector ψ_-, is negative. But the existence of particles with

105

negative energy cannot be admitted, for various compelling physical reasons:

(1) If such particles existed, they would allow violations of the principle of causality: *e.g.*, supposing they were emitted by the earth and absorbed by the sun, we should find the earth getting warmer *before* the sun parted with its energy!

(2) In a collision between a particle of negative energy and a system of positive energy, such as a hydrogen atom, it would be possible for the negative particle to gain momentum and at the same time impart energy and momentum to the atom, without violating the conservation of energy and momentum. Thus the unphysical possibility of obtaining unlimited amounts of energy from virtually nothing would be realized.

(3) Empirically, we know that there is a state of lowest energy, the vacuum, to which, by convention, zero energy is attributed. If particles with negative energy existed, there would be no such state of lowest energy.

It must be admitted, therefore, that the vector ψ_- cannot be associated with any physical state. Nevertheless this additional solution of the eigenvalue problem, allowed by the special theory of relativity, cannot simply be rejected.

To resolve this dilemma, we introduce a square root of the unit operator C, which has the property of anti-commuting with $(1-\dot{\mathbf{q}}^2/c^2)^{\frac{1}{2}}$, though commuting with $\mathbf{q}$ and $\dot{\mathbf{q}}$:

$$C^2 = 1,$$

$$(1-\dot{\mathbf{q}}^2/c^2)^{\frac{1}{2}}C + C(1-\mathbf{q}^2/c^2)^{\frac{1}{2}} = 0,$$

$$\mathbf{q}C - C\mathbf{q} = \dot{\mathbf{q}}C - C\dot{\mathbf{q}} = 0.$$

These relations are supposed to hold for uncharged and charged particles, whether there is an electromagnetic field or not. Supposing, however, that the particle is uncharged, or that there is no electromagnetic field, $H = mc^2(1-\dot{\mathbf{q}}^2/c^2)^{\frac{1}{2}}$, so $HC + CH = 0$, and

$$H(C\psi_-) = -CH\psi_- = c(m^2c^2+\mathbf{k}^2)^{\frac{1}{2}}(C\psi_-).$$

Thus there are two vectors, ψ_+ and $C\psi_-$, which are eigenvectors of H and correspond to the same *positive* eigenvalue $c(m^2c^2+\mathbf{k}^2)^{\frac{1}{2}}$.

Usually ψ_+ and $C\psi_-$ are distinct, and are therefore associated with distinct physical entities. If we agree that ψ_+ is associated with a particular particle, we shall say also that $C\psi_-$ is associated with the corresponding *anti-particle*. The existence of anti-particles was a prediction of relativistic quantum mechanics, first made by Dirac. All particles in nature have anti-particles: for instance, the positron is the anti-particle of the electron and the negative pion is the anti-particle of the positive pion. Only the photon and the neutral pion have anti-particles which cannot be distinguished from the particles themselves $(C\psi_- = \psi_+)$.

Supposing now that we are concerned with a charged particle in an electromagnetic field, there will still be eigenvectors ψ_+ and ψ_- of H, with eigenvalues E_+ and E_- which approach the values $c(m^2c^2+\mathbf{k}^2)^{\frac{1}{2}}$ and $-c(m^2c^2+\mathbf{k}^2)^{\frac{1}{2}}$, respectively, as the field tends to vanish:

$$H\psi_+ = E_+\psi_+,$$
$$H\psi_- = E_-\psi_-.$$

The eigenvector ψ_- is not physically admissible as it stands, but becomes so when multiplied by the operator C. For let

$$H' = mc^2(1-\dot{\mathbf{q}}^2/c^2)^{-\frac{1}{2}}-e\phi,$$
$$\mathbf{p}' = m\dot{\mathbf{q}}(1-\dot{\mathbf{q}}^2/c^2)^{-\frac{1}{2}}-e\mathbf{A}.$$

Then

$$\mathbf{p}'(C\psi_-) = -C\mathbf{p}\psi_-$$

and

$$H'(C\psi_-) = -CH\psi_- = -E_-(C\psi_-).$$

Hence, if

$$\psi'_- = C\psi_-, \qquad E' = -E_-,$$

then

$$H'\psi'_- = E'\psi'_-,$$

where

$$H' = \{m^2c^2+(\mathbf{p}'+e\mathbf{A}/c)^2\}^{\frac{1}{2}}-e\phi.$$

Thus ψ'_- is the eigenvector of H', which is the Hamiltonian of a particle with mass m and charge $-e$, i.e., the anti-particle corresponding to the particle of the original Hamiltonian H.

The operator C, which is called the *charge conjugation* operator, has the same properties as the operator, also denoted by C, introduced in 1.4. For, it follows from $\mathbf{q}H - H\mathbf{q} = i\hbar\dot{\mathbf{q}}$ and $\mathbf{q}H' - H'\mathbf{q} = i\hbar\dot{\mathbf{q}}$ that

$$C(i\hbar\dot{\mathbf{q}}) = C(\mathbf{q}H - H\mathbf{q}) = -(\mathbf{q}H' - H'\mathbf{q})C = -i\hbar\dot{\mathbf{q}}C,$$

and hence

$$Ci + iC = 0.$$

This result implies that the operator $\mathbf{i}$, which appears in non-relativistic as well as relativistic quantum mechanics, should not be regarded as an imaginary multiple of the unit operator, but as an operator in its own right, just as was suggested in 1.4.

Ex 19: Prove that $q_\alpha p'_\beta - p'_\beta q_\alpha = i\hbar\delta_{\alpha\beta}$ is a consequence of $q_\alpha p_\beta - p_\beta q_\alpha = i\hbar\delta_{\alpha\beta}$.

7.3 *Dirac's Theory of Electronic Spin*

Dirac's theory of the electron is based on a special interpretation of the square root in the expression for the energy. It is assumed that (in the absence of the electromagnetic field)

$$(m^2c^2 + \mathbf{p}^2)^{\frac{1}{2}} = mc\beta + \mathbf{p} \cdot \boldsymbol{\alpha},$$

where β and $\boldsymbol{\alpha}$ are operators independent of m and $\mathbf{p}$, and commuting with $\mathbf{q}$ and $\mathbf{p}$. To verify the existence of such operators, we square the above equation and obtain

$$m^2c^2 + \mathbf{p}^2 = m^2c^2\beta^2 + p_1{}^2\alpha_1{}^2 + p_2{}^2\alpha_2{}^2 + p_3{}^2\alpha_3{}^2$$

$$+ mc\{\beta, \mathbf{p} \cdot \boldsymbol{\alpha}\} + p_1 p_2\{\alpha_1, \alpha_2\} + p_2 p_3\{\alpha_2, \alpha_3\} + p_3 p_1\{\alpha_3, \alpha_1\},$$

where $\{A, B\}$ as usual means $AB + BA$. This equation is satisfied identically if and only if β and $\boldsymbol{\alpha}$ satisfy

$$\beta^2 = \alpha_1{}^2 = \alpha_2{}^2 = \alpha_3{}^2 = 1,$$

$$\{\beta, \boldsymbol{\alpha}\} = \{\alpha_1, \alpha_2\} = \{\alpha_2, \alpha_3\} = \{\alpha_3, \alpha_1\} = 0.$$

Let us write

$$\sigma_1 = -i\alpha_2\alpha_3, \quad \sigma_2 = -i\alpha_3\alpha_1, \quad \sigma_3 = -i\alpha_1\alpha_2;$$

then
$$\sigma_1{}^2 = -\alpha_2\alpha_3\alpha_2\alpha_3 = \alpha_3\alpha_2{}^2\alpha_3 - \alpha_3{}^2 = 1;$$
similarly, $\sigma_2{}^2 = 1$ and
$$\sigma_1\sigma_2 = -\alpha_2\alpha_1 = i\sigma_3 = \alpha_3\alpha_1\alpha_2\alpha_3 = -\sigma_2\sigma_1.$$

These are the fundamental relations satisfied by the Pauli matrices which, as we saw in 5.3, are used in representing the spin $\mathbf{S} = \tfrac{1}{2}\hbar\boldsymbol{\sigma}$ of a particle of spin half.

If we define
$$\beta' = -i\alpha_1\alpha_2\alpha_3,$$
then
$$\boldsymbol{\alpha} = \beta'\boldsymbol{\sigma} = \boldsymbol{\sigma}\beta',$$
$$\beta'^2 = 1, \quad \{\beta, \beta'\} = 0.$$

Thus β, β' and $\beta'' = -i\beta\beta'$ constitute a second set of Pauli matrices which commute with the spin matrices. The formula
$$(m^2c^2 + \mathbf{p}^2)^{\frac{1}{2}} = mc\beta + \mathbf{p}\cdot\boldsymbol{\sigma}\beta'$$
shows that the operator
$$\sigma_p = \mathbf{p}\cdot\boldsymbol{\sigma}/|\mathbf{p}|$$
(where $|\mathbf{p}|$ is the square root of $\mathbf{p}^2$ whose eigenvalues are all positive) commutes with $(m^2c^2 + \mathbf{p}^2)^{\frac{1}{2}}$, and hence with the energy. Since $\sigma_p{}^2 = \mathbf{p}^2/\mathbf{p}^2 = 1$, the eigenvalues of σ_p are $+1$ and -1. Thus there are, in all, *four* independent vectors which satisfy
$$H\psi = c(m^2c^2 + \mathbf{k}^2)^{\frac{1}{2}}\psi, \quad \mathbf{p}\psi = \mathbf{k}\psi.$$
They are ψ_{++}, ψ_{+-}, $\psi'_{-+} = C\psi_{-+}$ and $\psi'_{--} = C\psi_{--}$, which have the properties
$$\sigma_p\psi_{++} = \psi_{++}, \qquad \sigma_p\psi_{+-} = -\psi_{+-},$$
$$\sigma_p\psi'_{-+} = \psi'_{-+}, \qquad \sigma_p\psi'_{--} = -\psi'_{--}.$$
Of these, ψ_{++} and ψ_{+-} are associated with particles, with spins parallel and anti-parallel to the momentum $\mathbf{p}$, respectively; ψ'_{-+} and ψ'_{--} are associated with anti-particles, with spins parallel and anti-parallel to the momentum.

From the relation $\{C, i\} = 0$ and
$$\{C, (m^2c^2 + \mathbf{p}^2)^{\frac{1}{2}}\} = \{C, \mathbf{p}\} = 0,$$

valid when there is no electromagnetic field, it is easy to see that C commutes with $\boldsymbol{\alpha}$, but anti-commutes with β, $\boldsymbol{\sigma}$, and β'. It is easy to find four-dimensional matrices which have all the required properties, e.g.,

$$\alpha_1 = \begin{bmatrix} 0 & 1 & 0 & 0 \\ 1 & 0 & 0 & 0 \\ 0 & 0 & 0 & -1 \\ 0 & 0 & -1 & 0 \end{bmatrix}, \quad \alpha_2 = \begin{bmatrix} 1 & 0 & 0 & 0 \\ 0 & -1 & 0 & 0 \\ 0 & 0 & -1 & 0 \\ 0 & 0 & 0 & 1 \end{bmatrix},$$

$$\alpha_3 = \begin{bmatrix} 0 & 0 & 1 & 0 \\ 0 & 0 & 0 & 1 \\ 1 & 0 & 0 & 0 \\ 0 & 1 & 0 & 0 \end{bmatrix}, \quad \beta = \begin{bmatrix} 0 & 0 & -i & 0 \\ 0 & 0 & 0 & -i \\ i & 0 & 0 & 0 \\ 0 & i & 0 & 0 \end{bmatrix}.$$

Ex 20: Show how to resolve an arbitrary vector ψ, satisfying $H\psi = (m^2c^2+\mathbf{k}^2)^{\frac{1}{2}}\psi$ and $\mathbf{p}\psi = \mathbf{k}\psi$, into components ψ_{++}, ψ_{+-}, ψ'_{-+} and ψ'_{--}, given by

$$\psi_{++} = \tfrac{1}{4}(1+\sigma_p)[1+(mc\beta+\mathbf{k}\cdot\boldsymbol{\alpha})/(m^2c^2+\mathbf{k}^2)^{\frac{1}{2}}]\psi,$$
$$\psi_{+-} = \tfrac{1}{4}(1-\sigma_p)[1+(mc\beta+\mathbf{k}\cdot\boldsymbol{\alpha})/(m^2c^2+\mathbf{k}^2)^{\frac{1}{2}}]\psi,$$
$$\psi'_{-+} = \tfrac{1}{4}C(1+\sigma_p)[1-(mc\beta-\mathbf{k}\cdot\boldsymbol{\alpha})/(m^2c^2+\mathbf{k}^2)^{\frac{1}{2}}]\psi,$$
$$\psi'_{--} = \tfrac{1}{4}C(1-\sigma_p)[1-(mc\beta-\mathbf{k}\cdot\boldsymbol{\alpha})/(m^2c^2+\mathbf{k}^2)^{\frac{1}{2}}]\psi,$$

and interpret the result.

7.4 Charged Particle in an Electromagnetic Field

The generalization of the analysis of the last section for a non-vanishing electromagnetic field is easy. If e is the charge of the particle (*negative* for an electron), the Hamiltonian is assumed to be

$$H = c[mc\beta+(\mathbf{p}-e\mathbf{A}/c)\cdot\boldsymbol{\alpha}]+e\phi,$$

where $\boldsymbol{\alpha}$ and β satisfy the same (anti-)commutation relations as before. It should be noticed, however, that the expression $mc\beta+(\mathbf{p}-\mathbf{A}/c)\cdot\boldsymbol{\alpha}$ is not an exact square root of $m^2c^2+(\mathbf{p}-e\mathbf{A}/c)^2$, so that the above formula represents a definite deviation from the classical theory. In fact,

$$(H - e\phi)^2 = c^2[mc\beta + (\mathbf{p} - e\mathbf{A}/c) \cdot \boldsymbol{\alpha}]^2,$$
$$= m^2c^4 + c^2[(\mathbf{p} - e\mathbf{A}/c) \cdot \boldsymbol{\alpha}]^2$$

and

$$[(\mathbf{p} - e\mathbf{A}/c) \cdot \boldsymbol{\alpha}]^2 = (\mathbf{p} - e\mathbf{A}/c)^2 + \alpha_1\alpha_2[p_1 - eA_1/c, \; p_2 - eA_2/c]$$
$$+ \alpha_2\alpha_3[p_2 - eA_2/c, \; p_3 - eA_3/c] + \alpha_3\alpha_1[p_3 - eA_3/c, \; p_1 - eA_1/c]$$
$$= (\mathbf{p} - e\mathbf{A}/c)^2 - (e\hbar/c)\boldsymbol{\sigma} \cdot \mathbf{B},$$

where $\mathbf{B}$ is the magnetic induction, since $\alpha_1\alpha_2 = i\sigma_3$, etc., and $[A_2, \; p_1] - [A_1, \; p_2] = i\hbar B_3$, etc. Thus $mc\beta + (\mathbf{p} - e\mathbf{A}/c) \cdot \boldsymbol{\alpha}$ is strictly a square root of $m^2c^2 + (\mathbf{p} - e\mathbf{A}/c)^2 - (e\hbar/c)\boldsymbol{\sigma} \cdot \mathbf{B}$, and in a non-relativistic approximation we would have

$$H \approx mc^2 + \tfrac{1}{2}[(\mathbf{p} - e\mathbf{A}/c)^2 - (e\hbar/c)\boldsymbol{\sigma} \cdot \mathbf{B}]/m + e\phi.$$

The additional term $-e\hbar\boldsymbol{\sigma} \cdot \mathbf{B}/(2mc)$ in the energy may be interpreted as meaning that the electron has an intrinsic magnetic moment, equal to

$$\boldsymbol{\mu} = -e\hbar\boldsymbol{\sigma}/(2mc).$$

This is a prediction of Dirac's theory which is well substantiated by experiment. Note that $-e$ is positive for the electron.

A problem which will be discussed subsequently concerns the motion of a charged particle in a central electrostatic field. The field is then given by

$$\mathbf{A} = 0, \quad \phi = -(Kc/e)r^{-1},$$

where K is a constant and $r^2 = \mathbf{q}^2$, where $\mathbf{q}$ is the displacement of the particle from a fixed point $\mathbf{q}_0$. In the application to the hydrogen atom, $\mathbf{q}_0$ will be the centre of mass of the atom. The problem is to determine the eigenvalues of H, where

$$H = c(mc\beta + \mathbf{p} \cdot \boldsymbol{\alpha} - K/r).$$

It will be found advantageous, however, to consider first the quantization of the angular momentum.

7.5 *Angular Momentum States*

The total angular momentum of the particle of spin half is

$$\mathbf{J} = \mathbf{L} + \mathbf{S},$$

$$\mathbf{L} = \mathbf{x} \wedge \mathbf{p}, \quad \mathbf{S} = \tfrac{1}{2}\hbar\boldsymbol{\sigma}.$$

We wish to show first that $\mathbf{J}$ commutes with the energy H (for a particle in a central field). As $\mathbf{L}$ commutes with r, and $\boldsymbol{\sigma}$ commutes with β and β' (where $\boldsymbol{\alpha} = \beta'\boldsymbol{\sigma}$), it is sufficient to show that $\mathbf{J}$ commutes with $\mathbf{p} \cdot \boldsymbol{\sigma}$. But

$$[L_3, \ \mathbf{p} \cdot \boldsymbol{\sigma}] = i\hbar(p_2\sigma_1 - p_1\sigma_2),$$

$$[S_3, \ \mathbf{p} \cdot \boldsymbol{\sigma}] = i\hbar(p_1\sigma_2 - p_2\sigma_1),$$

and so J_3 commutes with $\mathbf{p} \cdot \boldsymbol{\sigma}$; similarly, J_1 and J_2 commute with $\mathbf{p} \cdot \boldsymbol{\sigma}$. Thus H, J_3 and $\mathbf{J}^2$ all commute with one another, and have simultaneous eigenvectors:

$$H\psi = E\psi, \quad J_3\psi = j_3\hbar\psi, \quad \mathbf{J}^2\psi = j(j+1)\hbar^2\psi,$$

where, according to 5.4, j_3 and j both take either integral values, or half odd integral eigenvalues, and $-j \leqq j_3 \leqq j$. Now $j_3 = l_3 + s_3$, where l_3 and s_3 are eigenvalues of $L_3/\hbar$ and $S_3/\hbar$, respectively; and, as l_3 is integral and $s_3 = \pm\tfrac{1}{2}$, j_3 must take half odd integral eigenvalues only. Therefore, j also takes only half odd integral eigenvalues.

Ex 21: Show that $j = l + \tfrac{1}{2}$ or $j = l - \tfrac{1}{2}$, where $l(l+1)$ is the eigenvalue of $\mathbf{L}^2/\hbar^2$.

It follows from the above example that the eigenvalues of

$$\mathbf{L} \cdot \mathbf{S} = \tfrac{1}{2}(\mathbf{J}^2 - \mathbf{L}^2 - \mathbf{S}^2)$$

are $\tfrac{1}{2}[(l\pm\tfrac{1}{2})(l\pm\tfrac{1}{2}+1) - l(l+1) - \tfrac{3}{4}]\hbar^2$, i.e., $\tfrac{1}{2}l\hbar^2$ and $-\tfrac{1}{2}(l+1)\hbar^2$. This can also be proved by using the result

$$(\mathbf{L} \cdot \mathbf{S} - \tfrac{1}{2}l\hbar^2)[\mathbf{L} \cdot \mathbf{S} + \tfrac{1}{2}(l+1)\hbar^2]\psi = 0$$

which, in view of the relation $\mathbf{L} \cdot \mathbf{S} = \tfrac{1}{2}\hbar L_\sigma$, was proved in 5.5. Another important result, which we shall borrow from 5.5, is

$$(\mathbf{L} \cdot \mathbf{S} + \tfrac{1}{2}\hbar^2)\mathbf{q} \cdot \mathbf{S} + \mathbf{q} \cdot \mathbf{S}(\mathbf{L} \cdot \mathbf{S} + \tfrac{1}{2}\hbar^2) = 0.$$

From this it follows that, if

$$\Lambda = -(2\mathbf{L} \cdot \mathbf{S} + \hbar^2)/\hbar + 2iK\mathbf{q} \cdot \mathbf{S}\beta'/r,$$

where K is any numerical constant and $\beta'^2 = 1$, then

$$\Lambda^2 = (2\mathbf{L} \cdot \mathbf{S} + \hbar^2)^2/\hbar^2 - K^2\hbar^2.$$

Thus the eigenvalues of Λ^2 are $[(l+1)^2 - K^2]\hbar^2$ and $(l^2 - K^2)\hbar^2$, and, as $\Lambda = -(2\mathbf{L} \cdot \mathbf{S} + \hbar^2)/\hbar$ when $K = 0$, the eigenvalues of Λ are λ_+ and λ_-, where

$$\lambda_+ = [(l+1)^2 - K^2]^{\frac{1}{2}}\hbar,$$
$$\lambda_- = -(l^2 - K^2)^{\frac{1}{2}}\hbar.$$

7.6 *Fine Structure of Levels of the Hydrogen Atom*

We are now in a position to determine the possible eigenvalues of the energy of a charged particle of spin half, in a central field. If E is any such eigenvalue and ψ is the corresponding eigenvector,

$$H\psi/c = (mc\beta + \mathbf{p} \cdot \mathbf{\alpha} - K/r)\psi = E\psi/c.$$

Let us set

$$\psi = (E/c + mc\beta + \mathbf{p} \cdot \mathbf{\alpha} + K/r)\chi;$$

then χ satisfies

$$(E/c + K/r)^2\chi = (m^2c^2 + \mathbf{p}^2 + [\mathbf{p} \cdot \mathbf{\alpha}, K/r])\chi$$
$$= (m^2c^2 + \mathbf{p}^2 + i\hbar K\mathbf{\alpha} \cdot \mathbf{q}/r^3)\chi.$$

Now, as shown in 4.5,

$$\mathbf{p}^2 = p_r^2 + \mathbf{L}^2/r^2,$$

and, as

$$2\mathbf{L} \cdot \mathbf{S}(2\mathbf{L} \cdot \mathbf{S} + \hbar^2) = \mathbf{L}^2\hbar^2,$$

it follows that

$$\mathbf{p}^2 = p_r^2 + 2\mathbf{L} \cdot \mathbf{S}(2\mathbf{L} \cdot \mathbf{S} + \hbar^2)/(\hbar^2 r^2).$$

Also,

$$\mathbf{\alpha} \cdot \mathbf{q} = \mathbf{\sigma} \cdot \mathbf{q}\beta' = 2\mathbf{q} \cdot \mathbf{S}\beta'/\hbar.$$

Hence

$$(E^2/c^2 - m^2c^2)\chi = [p_r^2 - 2KE/(cr) + \Lambda(\Lambda + \hbar)/r^2]\chi,$$

with Λ defined as in the previous section. This is the relativistic counterpart of the non-relativistic equation

113

$$2mE_n\chi = [p_r^2 - 2Kmc/r + l(l+1)\hbar^2/r^2]\chi,$$

where E_n, the non-relativistic eigenvalue of the energy, is approximately $E - mc^2$.

The relativistic problem is thus reduced to the determination of the eigenvalues of the linear operator

$$A = p_r^2 - 2KE/(cr) + \Lambda(\Lambda + \hbar)/r^2.$$

The eigenvalues of Λ are already known from the last section, and the eigenvalues of

$$A = p_r^2 + 2a_1 b_1/r + b_1(b_1 - \hbar)/r^2$$

were found, for general values of a_1 and b_1, in 6.1. In this instance, we have

$$a_1 b_1 = -KE/c,$$
$$b_1 = (l^2 - K^2)^{\frac{1}{2}}\hbar \text{ or } -[(l+1)^2 - K^2]^{\frac{1}{2}}\hbar;$$

the eigenvalues of A are given by

$$a^{(n)} = -a_n^2,$$
$$a_n b_n = a_1 b_1 = -KE/c,$$
$$b_n = n\hbar + b_1 - \hbar \text{ if } b_1 > 0,$$
$$b_n = n\hbar - b_1 \text{ if } b_1 < 0,$$

where n is a positive integer. Hence

$$E^2/c^2 - m^2 c^2 = -K^2 E^2/(b_n^2 c^2),$$

where

$$b_n = (n-1)\hbar + (l^2 - K^2)^{\frac{1}{2}}\hbar$$

or

$$n\hbar + [(l+1)^2 - K^2]^{\frac{1}{2}}\hbar.$$

Thus we have, finally,

$$E = mc^2(1 + K^2/b_n^2)^{-\frac{1}{2}}.$$

In the application to the hydrogen atom, $K = e^2/(4\pi\hbar c)$ $= 1/137.04$, where e is the electronic charge (in Heaviside units); thus K^2 is small compared with 1, and b_n is almost, though not exactly, an integral multiple of $\hbar$. For a fixed value of $n+1$, and different values of l, one obtains slightly different values of b_n and hence of E. This is Dirac's theory of the observed fine structure of the energy levels of the hydrogen atom.

EXAMPLES VII

1. Investigate the quantum mechanics of an electron in a constant magnetic field $\mathbf{B}$ in the following way. Show that the vector potential is $\mathbf{A} = \frac{1}{2}\mathbf{B} \wedge \mathbf{x}$, so that the Hamiltonian is

$$H = c[mc\beta + \boldsymbol{\alpha} \cdot (\mathbf{p} - \tfrac{1}{2}e\mathbf{B} \wedge \mathbf{x}/c)].$$

Suppose $\mathbf{B}$ is along the x_3-axis and assume that the eigenvector of H, corresponding to the eigenvalue E, has the form

$$\psi = [(E/c) + mc\beta + \boldsymbol{\alpha} \cdot (\mathbf{p} - \tfrac{1}{2}e\mathbf{B} \wedge \mathbf{x}/c)]\chi.$$

Hence obtain the equation

$$(E/c)^2\chi = [m^2c^2 + \mathbf{p}^2 + \tfrac{1}{4}e^2B_3^2(x_1^2 + x_2^2)/c^2$$
$$+ i\hbar e B_3 \alpha_1 \alpha_2/c - eB_3 L_3/c]\chi,$$

and show that

$$(E/c)^2 = m^2c^2 + p_3'^2 + [n|eB_3| - (l_3 \pm 1)eB_3]\hbar/c,$$

where p'_3 is the eigenvalue of p_3, n is a positive integer, and $l_3\hbar$ is the eigenvalue of L_3 (so l_3 is an integer). Prove that $n \geq |l_3| + 1$.

2. Investigate in a similar way the behaviour of the electron in a constant electric field, for which $\mathbf{A} = 0$ but $\phi = -\mathbf{E} \cdot \mathbf{x}$.

3. The neutrino is a massless neutral particle of spin half, represented by a vector ψ which always satisfies $\beta'\psi = \psi$. Show that the spin of the neutrino is always anti-parallel to its momentum, but that the spin of the anti-neutrino is always parallel to its momentum.

4. Show that, if the co-ordinate axes are rotated through an angle θ about the x_3-axis, so that the new co-ordinates are

$$x'_1 = x_1 \cos\theta - x_2 \sin\theta,$$
$$x'_2 = x_2 \cos\theta + x_1 \sin\theta,$$
$$x'_3 = x_3,$$

and the matrices $\boldsymbol{\alpha}$ and β are unaffected by the rotation, a vector ψ representing a particle of spin half must be changed to

$$\psi' = [\cos\ (\tfrac{1}{2}\theta) - \alpha_1\alpha_2 \sin\ (\tfrac{1}{2}\theta)]\psi,$$

in order that Dirac's equation should retain the same form.

5. Show that the Lorentz transformation connecting the coordinates and times of two observers O and O', whose relative velocity is $c \tanh u$ along the x_1-axis, may be written

$$t' = t \cosh u - (x_1/c) \sinh u,$$
$$x'_1 = x_1 \cosh u - ct \sinh u,$$
$$x'_2 = x_2, \qquad x'_3 = x_3.$$

Verify that the vectors ψ and ψ' used by O and O' to represent a particle of spin half must be connected by the relation

$$\psi' = [\cosh\ (\tfrac{1}{2}u) - \alpha_1 \sinh\ (\tfrac{1}{2}u)]\psi$$
$$= \exp\ (-\tfrac{1}{2}u\alpha_1)\psi.$$

6. In advanced work, the matrices γ_λ ($\lambda = 0, 1, 2, 3$), defined by

$$\gamma_0 = \beta, \qquad \boldsymbol{\gamma} = \beta\boldsymbol{\alpha},$$

are used instead of β and $\boldsymbol{\alpha}$. Show that if $p_0 = H/c$, Dirac's equation for a free particle may be written

$$(\gamma_0 p_0 - \boldsymbol{\gamma} \cdot \mathbf{p})\psi = mc\psi,$$

and that

$$(\gamma_0 p_0 - \boldsymbol{\gamma} \cdot \mathbf{p})^2 = p_0^2 - \mathbf{p}^2.$$

Appendix: Dirac's Notation

The bra-ket notation, devised by Dirac and used by many readers of his well known text-book [17], is a simple modification of that which has been used so far. Instead of ψ, the *ket* $|>$ is used to denote an arbitrary normalized vector. The conjugate vector ψ^*, whose components are the complex conjugates of the components of ψ, is represented by the *bra* $<|$. The normalized eigenvector of A, which corresponds to the eigenvalue a, is represented by the ket $|a\rangle$. A common eigenvector of A and B, corresponding to the eigenvalues a and b, respectively, is represented by $|a, b\rangle$. The scalar product of the vectors $\phi = |a\rangle$ and $\psi = |b\rangle$ is $\phi^*\psi = \langle a|b\rangle$. The following equations will be sufficient to illustrate the uses of this notation

$$A|a^{(j)}\rangle = a^{(j)}|a^{(j)}\rangle,$$

$$A|a^{(j)}, b^{(k)}\rangle = a^{(j)}|a^{(j)}, b^{(k)}\rangle, \quad B|a^{(j)}b^{(k)}\rangle = b^{(k)}|a^{(j)}, b^{(k)}\rangle,$$

$$\langle a|b\rangle = \langle b|a\rangle^*,$$

$$\langle a|B|b\rangle = b\langle a|b\rangle,$$

$$\langle a|C|b\rangle = \langle b|C^*|a\rangle^*.$$

The following equivalences should be noticed;

$$\langle a^{(k)}|b^{(l)}\rangle = \phi^{(k)*}\psi^{(l)} = \Sigma_j\phi_j^{(k)*}\psi_j^{(l)} = (\phi^{(k)}, \psi^{(l)}),$$

$$\langle a|C|b\rangle = \phi^*C\psi = \Sigma_j\Sigma_k\phi^*_jC_{jk}\psi_k = (\phi, C\psi).$$

References

[1] M. Planck, Deutsch. Phys. Gesell. Verh. **2**, 202, 237 (1900).
[2] A. Einstein, Ann. d. Physik **20**, 199 (1906).
[3] L. de Broglie, Contes Rendus, **177**, 507 (1923); **179**, 39 (1924).
[4] E. Schrödinger, Ann. d. Physik, **79**, 361, 489 (1926).
[5] M. Planck, *The Universe in the Light of Modern Physics*, G. Allen and Unwin Ltd: London (1931).
[6] P. A. Schlipp (Editor), *Albert Einstein: Philosopher Scientist*, Tudor Pub. Co: New York (1951).
[7] L. de Broglie, J. Phys. Rad. **20**, 963 (1959).
[8] E. Schrödinger, Nuov. Cim. X, **1**, 5 (1955).
[9] L. Janossy, Acta. Phys. Hungar. **1**, 423 (1952).
[10] D. Bohm and J. P. Vigier, Phys. Rev. **96**, 208 (1954).
[11] W. Heisenberg, Zeits. f. Phys. **33**, 879 (1925).
[12] M. Born and P. Jordan, Zeits. f. Phys. **34**, 858 (1925).
[13] W. Heisenberg, M. Born and P. Jordan, Zeits. f. Phys. **35**, 557 (1926).
[14] E. Schrödinger, Ann. d. Physik, **79**, 734 (1926).
[15] M. Born, Zeits. f. Physik **37**, 863; **38**, 803 (1926).
[16] N. Bohr, Phys. Rev. **48**, 696 (1935).
[17] See P. A. M. Dirac, *Quantum Mechanics*, Oxford Univ. Press (1935); also, Proc. Roy. Soc. A **114**, 243, 710 (1927).
[18] W. Heisenberg and W. Pauli, Zeitsch. f. Physik, **56**, (1929); **59**, 169 (1930).
[19] M. Born and P. Jordan, *Elementare Quantenmechanik*, Springer: Berlin (1930).
[20] E. Schrödinger, Proc. Roy. Irish Acad, A **46**, 9, 183 (1940); **47**, 53 (1941).
[21] L. Infeld and T. E. Hull, Rev. Mod. Phys. **23**, 21 (1951).
[22] H. S. Green, Phys. Rev. **90**, 270 (1953); Nuclear Physics, **54**, 565 (1964).
[23] H. S. Green, Nuovo Cimento, X, **9**, 880 (1958).